ADAM'S RIB

THE MGM LIBRARY OF FILM SCRIPTS

Ninotchka

North by Northwest

Adam's Rib

In preparation:

A Night at the Opera

A Day at the Races

Singin' in the Rain

Adam's Rib

A VIKING FILM BOOK

Screenplay by Ruth Gordon and Garson Kanin

NEW YORK / *The Viking Press*

© 1949, Loew's Incorporated
All rights reserved
Published in 1972 in a hardbound and paperbound
edition by The Viking Press, Inc.
625 Madison Avenue, New York, N.Y. 10022
Published simultaneously in Canada by
The Macmillan Company of Canada Limited
SBN 670-10477-9 (hardbound)
    670-01934-8 (paperbound)
Library of Congress catalog card number: 70-172940
Printed in U.S.A.

CREDITS

Production	Metro-Goldwyn-Mayer
Produced by	Lawrence Weingarten
Directed by	George Cukor
Written by	Ruth Gordon and Garson Kanin
Music by	Miklos Rozsa
Song: "Farewell, Amanda" by	Cole Porter
Director of Photography	George J. Folsey, A.S.C.
Art Directors	Cedric Gibbons and William Ferrari
Set decorations by	Edwin B. Willis
Associate	Henry W. Grace
Special effects by	A. Arnold Gillespie
Film Editor	George Boemler
Recording supervisor	Douglas Shearer
Miss Hepburn's costumes	Walter Plunkett
Hair styles	Sydney Guilaroff
Make-up	Jack Dawn
Length	9070 ft.
Time	101 minutes
Released	1949

CAST

ADAM BONNER	Spencer Tracy
AMANDA BONNER	Katharine Hepburn
DORIS ATTINGER	Judy Holliday
WARREN ATTINGER	Tom Ewell
KIP LURIE	David Wayne
BERYL CAIGHN	Jean Hagen
OLYMPIA LAPERE	Hope Emerson
GRACE	Eve March

NOTE

Square brackets indicate those parts of the original script that were not filmed; footnotes show important additions in the completed film. Minor variations that do not affect plot or characterization have not been documented.

ADAM'S RIB

"MAN AND WIFE"*

Fade in:
Exterior, Madison Square, New York City, 1949
Long Shot

The atmosphere, though metropolitan, is gentle. Spring is here. The people and the pigeons who share this spot are not molesting one another as much as usual. From offscreen, an amplified GONG *begins to strike the hour of five.*

Close Shot—the Clock

It vibrates slightly with each peal. Above it, the legend: "Gotham Life Insurance Company Building." The CAMERA *tips downward on the last chimes. So organized is this organization, that already the beginning of the long stream of employees has begun to trickle out of the building.*

Medium Shot

[The swiftly moving crowd. The CAMERA DOLLIES *forward until we spy a woman standing in the marble corner of the hall, eyeing the outcoming folk. Before we notice her we notice the hat she wears, sprouting three tall inverted flowers. She is obviously attempting to conceal herself. She watches. She watches. In the foreground of the* SHOT, *the blur of figures hurrying by.*

Medium Shot

A wide set of glass doors. Still they come, now in a thickening crush.

Close Shot—the Woman, *watching, the lower half of her face covered by a folded newspaper. Suddenly, a spasm of recog-*

---

* The name of the film was changed from *Man and Wife* to *Adam's Rib*.

1

nition. *The newspaper comes away from her face and she takes a step forward. (The movement swells the image on the screen.) We are afforded a better look at the sweet-faced young woman, harassed and haunted, her eyes glistening with surprised excitement at her own present activity.*

Close Shot
The chinless profile of a man. The CAMERA PANS *into:*

Medium Shot—the Man, *as he stops at a newsstand in the lobby of the building to buy a paper.*

Medium Shot—the Woman, *still watching. She raises the folded newspaper again to mask herself.*

Medium Shot—the Man, *at the newsstand. He completes the transaction and starts off. Reaching the sidewalk, he turns left.*

Medium Shot—the Watching Woman
She begins to move, the CAMERA FOLLOWING. *She goes past the newsstand, out onto the sidewalk, and turns left. It is obvious that she is following the man (and that the* CAMERA *is following her). He moves with the throng which seems to be going in one direction only and, in a way known only to experienced cliff dwellers, he open his newspaper as he walks, folds it, and reads as he moves. A few steps and he begins his descent into the subway. The woman is following him with all the speed she can muster on two-and-a-half-inch heels. She accelerates in a panic of fear of losing the scent and follows him down, down, down. The* CAMERA STOPS. *Both of our figures are part of the crowd now, but for a fleeting moment we see the three flowers bobbing about on the surface of heads.*

Dissolve to:

Interior, IRT Subway—Medium Shot

It is jam-packed. There is no possibility of making room for even one more. The roar of the car stops for a moment as does its vibration. About one hundred fifty more passengers squeeze in. The followed man twists into:

Close Shot—the Man, *still reading his paper.*

Close Shot—the Woman, *craning so as not to lose sight of her quarry.*

Medium Shot

The man in the foreground. The woman, mainly identified by her flowered hat, in the background. Some pushing goes on. The man is twisted into profile. The woman, after a long and confusing spin, winds up directly behind him. They are back to back. They are touching. The woman looks about the car, worried. She seems to have lost him. Finally, over her shoulder, she recognizes his unmistakable ear. She turns away quickly and buries her face between her paper and her purse. The man squints out of the subway car window, recognizes the approach to his stop, and begins to thread his way out. The woman, after a moment, follows.][1]

[1] In the film, instead:

The woman (DORIS ATTINGER) is pacing back and forth in Madison Square, eating a candy bar. She pauses and looks at her watch. The man, WARREN ATTINGER, is seen coming out of the building in a crowd; he pauses on the steps of the building and straightens his tie. DORIS sees him and holds her hand up at the side of her face so he won't see her. ATTINGER comes across the street toward DORIS, who conceals herself around the corner of a newsstand, pulling a veil down over her face. ATTINGER buys a paper at the newsstand and goes off to the subway, followed by DORIS. (See film still 1.) ATTINGER goes through the turnstile, whistling at a pretty woman passing through, followed by DORIS. A man brushes her and knocks her purse out of her hand; it has partially opened, lying on the floor, and we see a gun inside. She quickly picks it up, and is pushed by the crowd into a subway car as the CONDUCTOR says, "Step back. Right into the car. Step lively. Back into the car. Right in. That's all. That's all. Take the next train. Step back, please."

Dissolve to:

Exterior, West Seventy-second Street—Medium Shot—the Subway Staircase

The man comes by moving swiftly. A moment passes, the woman comes by.

Dissolve to:

Exterior, West Seventy-seventh Street—Medium Long Shot

We see the man coming toward CAMERA, *followed by the woman. He stops. She ducks into a doorway. He looks around, sees no one, continues on past the* CAMERA. *The woman emerges from her doorway and continues the chase.*

Exterior, around the Corner—Medium Full Shot—the Man, *walking slowly and deliberately, the* CAMERA TRUCKING. *In the background of the* SHOT, *we see a part of the watching woman. [Now the man stops beside an alleyway. He gets out a cigarette and lights it. He looks around, then quickly ducks into the alley. The woman comes toward the* CAMERA *now, at break-neck speed. She runs into a:*

Close-up—the Woman, *looking carefully down the alley.]*

Medium Shot—the Man, *as he turns into a doorway. On the* CAMERA *side of the door is a sign which reads:*

DELIVERY ENTRANCE

213 W. 78 ST.

DELIVERIES ONLY

SUPT'S BELL TO YR. LEFT

THANK YOU!

NO SOLICITORS

THANK YOU!

The woman moves into the SHOT, *stealthily now, stalking her prey. [She looks through a barred basement window.*

4

Medium Shot, *through the barred window. The woman's gloved hand comes into the* SHOT. *It holds a small but deadly looking automatic pistol. With the back of her glove, the woman wipes away enough of the dust to see into the cellar hallway.]* The man touches one of a row of buttons. Again. He leans close to the wall and speaks into a house intercom. He smiles. He goes through a clicking door. The gloved hand leaves the SHOT, and, in a moment, the woman has entered the hallway. She opens the still-clicking door a few inches and holds it so with her foot.

Medium Shot—the Second-Floor Hallway—Shooting Down
The man rushes by. Offscreen we hear a signal knock—a door opening, a whisper, the door closing.
The woman ascends into the SHOT. *She comes toward the* CAMERA. *She stops and looks at a door.*

Extreme Close Shot—the Door
On it is painted "2-D."

Close Shot—the Woman
She brings forth the pistol, looks at it carefully, turns it to one side, to the other. She is trying to find the safety catch. She fails. She makes a gesture of petty impatience with herself. Now she opens her handbag and gets out a little manual. (It came with the pistol.) She studies a diagram, refers to the weapon—then back to the booklet. (See film still 2.) She turns a page—suddenly sees it all clearly. The safety catch is clicked, the manual put away. She gets a good grip on the pistol with her right hand, puts its muzzle near to the lock, closes her eyes, and fires once!—twice!—again! in swift succession. She kicks the door open and bounds into the room, the CAMERA FOLLOWING. *[The man stands to one side, a beautiful girl in his arms. Both are frozen with fear. The girl wears a black silk negligee.*
THE WOMAN *(in a snarl)*: My dear husband. My dear husband.

5

She fires again, this time at the couple. They break apart.
THE MAN *steps in front of* THE GIRL, *shielding her.* THE GIRL
begins to scream.

THE WOMAN: Shut up! Shut up, you!

*She moves into position to shoot around him and at the
girl. She fires.*

THE MAN (*moving forward*): Don't! No! Listen—please—Doris—
(*See film still 3.*)

She fires again. The bullet connects. THE MAN *grabs his
middle and pitches forward with a cry.* THE GIRL *screams.*
THE WOMAN *whirls and fires at her. A lamp crashes to the
floor.*

THE WOMAN: No!

THE MAN (*crying*): I'm done—you didn't even—I'm done—

She fires again at the moaning man.

THE MAN: No more—no more—please—no more—

She tries to fire again; the pistol clicks. She drops it. THE
MAN *suddenly lies still on the floor.* THE GIRL *makes her way
out of the room and goes down the hall, yelling for help.*]²
THE WOMAN *goes to the still form on the floor and looks down
at it tenderly. Suddenly, she falls to her knees and sobs. (See
film still 4.)* [*The* CAMERA MOVES IN SLOWLY. *Offscreen, a
siren is heard coming toward us. At a given point the move-*

---

² In the film, instead:

ATTINGER and BERYL CAIGHN are seen embracing on the couch. They
jump up in terror.

ATTINGER: Now look here, Doris—

DORIS: Shut up, you! Shut up!

She points the gun at him and closes her eyes, saying "My dear husband."
ATTINGER backs into a corner and tries to hide behind a drape as she fires
the gun. BERYL screams.

ATTINGER: D-D-Doris, please—please—oh, don't, don't Doris, don't.

DORIS, her eyes still closed, shoots twice. ATTINGER grabs his shoulder and
falls against the couch, saying "Oh." BERYL hides behind the phonograph,
screaming. ATTINGER leans against the back of the couch; another shot is
heard and he falls to the floor. DORIS is laughing and sobbing hysterically
as she fires the gun past BERYL, who is standing by the mantel; the shot
hits the lamp on a table. BERYL screams and runs out, crying "Help! Help!
Help! Help! Murder! Help!"

ment of the CAMERA *and the siren's* SOUND *cease abruptly. The* action freezes on the screen, *holds a moment. Now the* CAMERA PULLS BACK, *with speed.*

Montage—a Series of Shots, *following the course of the photo.*
1. *It is surrounded by a weird set of hieroglyphics, as by a newspaper make-up person.*
2. *Linotype keyboard, with flying fingers.*
3. *A press as it prints the photo and headline.*
4. *The page in paste-up.*
5. *The forms being locked.*
6. *The plate as it is mounted on the press.*
7. *The rolling presses.*
8. *The papers being loaded into trucks.*
9. *Bunches of papers hitting a sidewalk near a newsstand, the bunches being cut open at once.*
10. *A janitor walking along carrying about forty copies.*]

Dissolve to:
Interior, the Hallway of the Bonner Apartment
Medium Shot—near Apartment 804
[*A uniformed doorman comes through and drops two newspapers at the door. He touches the bell and moves on to the next apartment. The door to 804 opens—a maid reaches out and takes in the papers.*][3]

Interior, the Bonners' Apartment—Full Shot
A breakfast cart is in the foreground of the SHOT, *which angles from a balcony into the sitting room. The maid comes up the stairs with a breakfast tray set for two. She arranges it*

---

[3] In the film, the newspapers are placed on the floor. On the front page are pictures of DORIS, ATTINGER, and BERYL. Headlines read:

NEW YORK CHRONICLE
WIFE SHOOTS FICKLE MATE
IN PRESENCE OF LOVE RIVAL;
ARRESTED ON ASSAULT CHARGE

and the newspapers on the service. Now she pushes it down the hall, the CAMERA TRUCKING *before it. At the bedroom door, she stops.* THE CAMERA STOPS. *She knocks. She knocks again.*

A WOMAN'S VOICE *(from within)*: Okay!
The maid leaves.

Interior, the Bonners' Bedroom—Full Shot

The room in semidarkness. A figure opens the door and pulls the breakfast cart into the room and begins to draw the drapes. The first one lets in a bright streak of sunlight which falls on the bed nearest the window. The singular arrangement here is a pair of beds—one a double, one a single! The head of the reclining figure on the single retreats, turtle-fashion. The figure pushes the cart between the beds.

THE FIGURE *(to the bed, in a cheery female voice)*: Seven-thirty!
She goes out. We hear her gargling briefly.

[A Man's Voice *(hoarsely)*: That's right. Seven-thirty. You said it.]⁴
He rolls from his left side to his back, sits up, shakes his head, lies back, then rolls to his right side. The figure returns and hops into bed. Offscreen, a whistle blows, and we hear the faint sound of several alarm clocks going off. The city is waking up.

Medium Shot—Twin Beds

Meet AMANDA. AMANDA FARING BONNER. *Also known as Mrs. Bonner (to neighbors, doormen, and headwaiters). As Amanda Faring to others (of Boyd, Karsh, Faring and Wellman). As Miss Faring (to the staff there). As Maddo⁵ (to close friends), and as Pinkie (to her husband).*

⁴ In the film, instead:
ADAM: Hm? Oh. Mmm. You said it. You said it. Seven-thirty. Hm. Ummmm.
⁵ In an earlier draft of the script AMANDA and ADAM were called MADELEINE (MADDO for short) and NED.

Now he sits up, shaking his head again in an effort to start it ticking. This is ADAM I. BONNER *(to almost everyone). Also Pinky (to Maddo, also Pinkie).*

ADAM: Hello, Pinkie.

AMANDA: Hello, Pinky.

Simultaneously, they make the sound of a kiss at each other and reach for their respective glasses of fruit juice.

AMANDA: You feel all right?

ADAM: I don't know. Why?

AMANDA: You were making some noises in the night.

A pause as they finish their fruit juice—reach for newspapers and continue to breakfast and read at one and the same time.

ADAM *(immersed in his paper)*: I always do. Don't I? At least you always say I always do. How do I know?

AMANDA *(without looking up)*: You do, but not this kind.

ADAM: What kind?

AMANDA: Can't remember exactly, naturally, but sort of like ooooo-eegah! ooooo-eegah.

She emits a series of strange groans and grunts and whistles and wheezes.

Like that, sort of.

ADAM *(looking at her)*: You don't say.

AMANDA: Yes.

ADAM: Fascinating.

AMANDA *(she looks at him)*: What?

ADAM: I say I sound fascinating.

AMANDA *(her lovely smile shining)*: You'll do. *(They return to their papers and food.)* Hot dog!

ADAM: What?

AMANDA: Wait a second.

ADAM: What?

AMANDA: Woman shot her husband.

ADAM: Kill 'im?

AMANDA: Uh—just a second—I think she—uh—*(Disappointed)*: No.

ADAM: Shame.

AMANDA *(brightly)*: Condition critical, though.

ADAM: Congratulations.

AMANDA: Wow!

ADAM: What?

AMANDA: Wait a second.

ADAM: What?

AMANDA *(irritated)*: Oh, find it in yours.

ADAM *(ruffling through his paper and speaking sharply)*: It isn't *in* here!

AMANDA *(rattling)*: He was playing her fast and loose so she caught him out and popped him a few thirty-two calibers.

ADAM: Who?

AMANDA: This lady. This lady I've been telling you about. In the paper.

ADAM: Some lady.

He finds the story in his paper.

AMANDA: Served him right, the little two-timer.

[ADAM: This says he's six-one and weighs one-ninety. Little.][6]

AMANDA *(loftily)*: In spirit, I mean, of course. Little in spirit.

ADAM: I don't approve of people rushing around with pistols.

AMANDA: Depends who they're rushing at.

ADAM: Is that what they taught you at Yale Law School? *(She laughs)* Not funny.[7]

[AMANDA: Yes, you are.]

ADAM: Contempt for law is the first sign of—

A knock at the door.

AMANDA: Come in!

Close Shot—the Door, *as* MARY *puts her head in.*

MARY: Better get crackin', you two. Heavy traffic today.

[6] In the film, instead:
ADAM: Um-um. Says here he's five-eleven, weighs one-eighty. Some little.
[7] In the film, Amanda precedes this by saying, "You're pretty fun—"

Medium Shot—the Room

[ADAM: Yuh.]

He and AMANDA *hop out of bed and make for their respective bathrooms.* MARY *begins to clear breakfast. Her eye catches the newspaper on* AMANDA's *bed, folded to the familiar photo with its story. She picks it up and reads it.*

MARY *(to the photo, in a singsong of encouragement)*: Atta girl!

Dissolve to:

Exterior, East River Drive—Two Shot—Amanda and Adam

She is driving their convertible, the top down. [*Both are talking at once. And from the radio, the* SOUND *of a voice reading out the market report.*

AMANDA:—but that doesn't mean that it's a law of nature it just means that the morals of women are—

ADAM:—the trouble is you won't listen, you're always so eager to hear what you have to say next—Look out!]

[*She pulls sharply to the right to let a speeder by.*

ADAM: All right, now. One at a time. Okay?

AMANDA: Okay. Me first.

ADAM *looks at her sharply, but resigns.*

ADAM: Go ahead.

AMANDA *leans forward and turns off the radio. In the background the Queensboro Bridge is receding, and to the right Peter Cooper, Stuyvesant Town, the U.N. It's a nice morning.*][8]

AMANDA: All I've been trying to say is this. Lots of things a man can do and in society's eyes it's all hunky-dory. A woman does the same things—the same, mind you, and she's an outcast.

ADAM: Finished?

AMANDA: No. Now I don't blame you personally, Adam, because this is so.

---

[8] In the film, as another car passes AMANDA, the driver blasts his horn at her.
AMANDA: Well, get by—big pig!
ADAM: Why don't you let him go by? He's simply—
AMANDA: He hogs the whole road.

11

ADAM: Thank you. That's large of you.

AMANDA: It's not your fault. All I say is why let this deplorable system seep into our courts of law, where women are supposed to be equal?

ADAM: If anything, females get advantages!

AMANDA: We don't want advantages! And we don't want prejudices!

[ADAM: Don't get excited.][9]

AMANDA: What did she do? She tried to keep her home intact.

ADAM: That's right. By killing her husband.

[AMANDA: She didn't kill him.

ADAM: She tried to. She missed.

AMANDA: What if he were a woman and she were a man—that's right—what if Mr. Attinger was Mrs. Attinger and Mrs. Attinger was Mr.—uh—

ADAM: Attinger?

AMANDA: Yes—*Mr.* Attinger. What then? Go ahead.

> *She turns the radio on. The market reports drone on. He turns it off again.*

ADAM: I can't follow your line.

AMANDA: Scot-free. She'd go scot-free. That is *he* would. Lennahan *did*!

ADAM: He *shouldn't* have, that's the whole—][10]

AMANDA *(mumbling)*: —the kind of thing that burns my goat!

ADAM: What?

AMANDA: My goat! My goat!

ADAM: A crime should be punished, not condoned.

AMANDA: If a woman commits it.

---

[9] In the film, instead:
ADAM: Oh, don't get excited, honey, and don't—
AMANDA: I'm not excited—
ADAM: —Oh, you're giving me the Bryn Mawr right—
[10] In the film, instead:
AMANDA: She didn't knock him off. He's alive. She didn't kill him.
ADAM: She tried—she missed.
AMANDA: Well, all right. Now, supposing—
ADAM: What do you want to do? Give her another shot at him?
AMANDA: No, I don't.

12

ADAM: Anybody.

[AMANDA: Then why aren't they?

He looks off.]

ADAM: Pull over—[pull over!

AMANDA: What?

ADAM: You're passing it!]

AMANDA: Oh! *(She swings over and stops the car abruptly. A shrieking of brakes just behind her. She looks back and waves a gay little salute, singing out in a cheery tone)* Sorry!

A taxi pulls around to pass her. As it does so the taxi driver calls out to AMANDA.

THE CABBIE: Oh, you lady drivers! You'll put me away yet!

He drives off. AMANDA *turns to* ADAM, *with a pained resigned, self-righteous, and pitying look.*

AMANDA: See?

ADAM: What?

AMANDA: He doesn't believe in women.

He leans over and they kiss. (See film still 5.) Behind them, the waiting traffic sets up a raucous complaint. AMANDA *and* ADAM *wait it out, kissing. Finally they break.*

AMANDA *(sexy)*: But you do, don't you? And you're an Assistant District Attorney, which makes it legal!

They kiss again.

ADAM *goes into the Court Building.* AMANDA *drives off, the* CAMERA FOLLOWING *until she is swallowed up in traffic. On the sidewalk, in the foreground, a pretzel vendor dusts his wares with a feather duster.*]

Interior, the Office of the New York County District Attorney— Full Shot[11]

The feel, at this hour, is lethargic. The room is split by a wood-glass partition. ADAM's *deputies,* DAVE *and* ROY *are*

---

[11] In the film, printing on the door reads:

ADAM BONNER
ASSISTANT
DISTRICT ATTORNEY

working at their desks in the outer part of the room. They are drinking office-made coffee. DAVE *is the younger, smoking a pipe.* ROY *lights a cigarette.* ADAM's *office is visible beyond. He comes in.*

DAVE: Morning[, sir].

ADAM: Hello, Dave. Everything down? *(He pours himself a cup of coffee from the Silex)*

DAVE: Just now. We've got five assaults, seven robberies, and I'm still counting.

ADAM: Well, you're young.

DAVE: Not for long. After all, Mommy's only got one pair of brains.

ADAM *goes into his own office, the* CAMERA FOLLOWING *him into:*

Medium Shot

He stands at his desk, flipping the morning's drop, and sipping his coffee. From offscreen, the voices of DAVE *and* ROY *are heard.*

ROY *(offscreen)*: I may give up smoking, you know that?

DAVE *(offscreen)*: What's this habeas corpus on 940A?

ROY *(offscreen)*: Search me.

DAVE *(offscreen)*: No sense to it.

ROY *(offscreen)*: On the other hand, why should I give up smoking if I enjoy it?

ADAM *(picking up a document, suddenly)*: Oh, no!

ROY *and* DAVE *appear in the doorway.*

DAVE: Something?

ADAM *(a whisper)*: Oh, mercy!

DAVE: What?

ADAM *(mumbling)*: The one case I don't want is the one case I get [(or "I've got")].

DAVE [*(or* ROY*)*]: Always the way, rule of the profession.

ADAM: But *this*—

DAVE: Which one?

14

ADAM (*disgustedly*): This hysterical Hannah that shot her husband. My wife feels—

ROY: A cinch. They already got you a full confession. That's the kind of case you bring your knitting. A cinch.

ADAM *goes to him.*

ADAM (*angrily*): A cinch, huh?

ROY (*taken aback*): What?

ADAM: You're not married to my wife, see?

ROY: How do you know?

ADAM (*in sudden anger*): A cinch, huh? I ought to poke you one, Roy.

A buzzer sounds on ADAM'*s desk. He flips a key.*

VOICE: Got a minute, Adam?

ADAM: Right now, chief. (*He stalks out*)

DAVE: A case of overwrought. Simple overwrought.

ROY: I notice guys doing things like that more and more. I've got a theory. Want to hear it? It's this: I think the human race is having a nervous breakdown.

Dissolve to:
[**Exterior, Lower Broadway—Full Shot,** including buildings, traffic, and a handkerchief-sized sky.][12]

Interior, Amanda's Office—Medium Shot
A small, old, neat room.

AMANDA *is standing in the bend of a tall bay window looking out over the Battery as she dictates to her secretary, a lady called* GRACE. *From the nearby East River the sounds of tug boats and ferries rise up to mingle with the clatter of business machines.*

AMANDA (*with some speed*): —which is why I am compelled to

[12] Instead, the corridor outside AMANDA's office. Printing on door at left and placard hanging at right on wall read:

3706	LAW OFFICES
AMANDA BONNER	OF
ATTORNEY AT LAW	AMANDA BONNER

return same to you for further revision. If this course seems to you unnecessarily exacting may I remind you that unless we obtain certiorari in the immediate future—*(She stops abruptly and turns into the room)* Grace—What do you think of a man who is unfaithful to his wife?

GRACE *(indulgently)*: Not nice.

AMANDA: All right. Now, what about a woman who is unfaithful to her husband?

GRACE *(outraged)*: Something terrible.

AMANDA: Aha!

GRACE: Aha what?

[AMANDA: In either case it's a sign the marriage is on the rocks but why the difference? Why "not nice" for one and "something terrible" for the other?][13]

GRACE: I don't make the rules.

AMANDA: You *do*. We *all* do.

> GRACE *is confused for a moment, looks down at her pad and reads:*

GRACE: Unless we obtain certiorari in the immediate future—
> AMANDA *turns back to the window and continues:*

AMANDA: The matter looks hopeless. I again urge you to study and consider United Zinc Co.—*(She suspends the speech, turns into the room again)* A boy sows a wild oat or two, the world winks. *(The phone rings)* A girl does the same—scandal. *(Phone rings again;* AMANDA *picks it up)* [Yes. . . . Hello, husband. Where you been keeping yourself?][14] *(She throws a shocked glance toward* GRACE *and speaks reprovingly into the phone)* Adam! . . . [What?

---

[13] In the film, instead:
AMANDA: Why the difference? Why the difference? Why "not nice" if he does it and "something terrible" if she does it?
[14] In the film, instead, AMANDA picks up the phone and says "Yeah?"
ADAM'S VOICE: Hello, honey.
AMANDA: Hello. Hello, husband.
ADAM'S VOICE: You've been on my mind, baby.
AMANDA: Where you been keeping yourself?
ADAM'S VOICE: I've been resting up after a hard—

16

. . . Yes . . . . Sure, go ahead.]¹⁵ *(Now she listens with widening interest)*

Interior, Adam's Office—Close Shot

ADAM *on the phone.*

ADAM: So the boss wants a fast conviction—and I'm just the boy to get it for him too, he says. *(He listens)*¹⁶ What? *(Listens some more)* [No, but I guess you'll be pretty proud of me when I finish downtrodding her—or trodding her down—how would you say it?]

Interior, Amanda's Office—Close Shot

AMANDA *on the phone. She's listening.*

AMANDA *(after a moment)*: It's an outrage. That's what I think . . . [What's so funny?]¹⁷

Interior, Adam's Office—Medium Shot

ADAM *on the phone. He is laughing now.*

ADAM: Nothing. You just sound so cute when you get causey. *(He pulls the phone from his ear suddenly)* [Ow!] *(He laughs again)* Hello. *(He hangs up)*

Interior, Amanda's Office—Medium Shot

Angling over GRACE *to* AMANDA *behind the desk. She moves to a cigarette box near the* CAMERA. *As she comes closer into*

---

¹⁵ In the film:
ADAM'S VOICE: You know the woman who shot her husband yesterday?
AMANDA: Yeah.
ADAM'S VOICE: Want a good laugh?
AMANDA: Sure, go ahead.
ADAM'S VOICE: Well, I'm elected. And I was going to ask the chief to let me off—if only on account of peace at home—
AMANDA: What?
¹⁶ In the film, he hears
AMANDA'S VOICE: You great big he-men make me sick.
¹⁷ In the film, instead:
ADAM'S VOICE: You're getting awfully dramatic, dear.
AMANDA: Why—why—what's so funny?

the SHOT *we see a new glint in her eyes. She gets a cigarette and lights it.*

AMANDA *(in a strangely changed voice)*: Grace—

GRACE: Yuh?

AMANDA: Did you ever hear of the straw that broke the camel's back?

GRACE: Many times.

AMANDA: Well, it just did it again. *(She points)* Right on that phone—the last straw on a female camel.

GRACE *(looks at the phone, too)*: Right on that phone.

AMANDA: Yeah. . . . Better write all this down.

GRACE: Go ahead.

AMANDA: There's a woman named—named—wait a second— *(She moves to the door and shouts out to her outer office)* [Get me the morning papers in here. Right away.][18] *(She moves back to Grace)* All right, whatever her name is—she shot her husband last night.

GRACE: Served him right.

AMANDA: I'm not joking, now. This is big.

GRACE: I see that.

AMANDA: One: find out where she is. Two: get me copies of whatever police and court records are available. Three: find out who's handling her. Probably Legal Aid Society—if that's it— let me talk to Rogers down there. *(GRACE is taking down like mad)* If she's privately defended—find out who and let me talk to them. Four: get Miss Bassett over at Women's Council for Equal Rights. Five: get my husband on the phone. Six: no, *don't* get my husband on the phone. *(An office boy comes in with the papers)* Thank you, Bobby.

BOBBY: Woman popped her ever-lovin'. You see that?

AMANDA: [Yes, thank you.][19] *(He goes.* AMANDA *is looking at the paper)* Attinger.

[18] Instead, in the film:
AMANDA: Hey, Bobby, bring me the morning papers in here right away, will you, please?
[19] In the film, instead:
AMANDA: Yeah. Thanks. Beat it.

18

GRACE: A-t-t-i-n-g-e-r?

AMANDA: That's it. Doris Attinger. Want to see her today sure. Without fail.

GRACE: What's going to happen?

AMANDA: Plenty!

> GRACE *goes.* AMANDA *moves to her desk and looks at the story again.*

[Extreme Close Shot—a Photo Layout

> *One shot is a picture of* MISS BERYL CAIGHN. *The other is a blown-up snapshot of the Attingers, in bathing suits—arms around each other, smiling broadly.*

AMANDA's VOICE *(offscreen)*:

"The little dog laughed
  To see such sport
And the dish ran away
  With the spoon."

Dissolve to:
Exterior, Polyclinic Hospital—Long Shot

> *In the middle foreground several signs read:* "HOSPITAL—QUIET"—"ZONE OF QUIET," *etc.*
>
> *In the near foreground two workers continue to rebuild the City of New York with automatic drills you can hear with your spine.*]

Dissolve to:
Interior, a Hospital Room—Medium Full Shot

> WARREN ATTINGER *is lying in bed, pale, and still suffering the effects of shock. His ear is bandaged, also his body. Sitting beside him is* BERYL. *At the foot of the bed,* ADAM, *wearing his topcoat. Also present are a male stenographer and a policeman.*[20]

---

[20] In the film:
ADAM: Hm. What—uh—what explanation have you got?

ATTINGER: She's crazy, that's all. *That's* the only explanation. Plain crazy. She's always been crazy, if you want a fact.

ADAM: Crazy when you married her?

ATTINGER: Certainly. A fruit cake.

ADAM: Why'd you marry her, then?

ATTINGER: How should I know? Who knows? Why'd you marry *yours*? Does anybody know?

ADAM: Just a moment, Mr. Attinger. Let's not get this going *too* free and easy. Now, *after* you have filed complaint and—

ATTINGER (*interrupting*): I been complainin' ever since the day I married her so go ahead, file it. She's nuts, that's my complaint. I like to see her put away somewheres, that's all. Out of my hair.

BERYL: Murderers running around. What kind of a town is this?

ADAM (*looking at her*): We don't have many murderers running around, Miss Caighn—but we have some things just as bad.

BERYL: You mean like *me*, huh? Listen, bub, I connect with you— you ain't over *my* head.

ADAM: Good.

ATTINGER: I'm going to get a lawyer on my own or somebody. I got to get her put away.

ADAM (*out of patience*): Now, look, pal. You're running way ahead of yourself. Just give us the background and the facts—I'll get the conviction on attempted murder, first-degree assault—however it seems best to the office to proceed. Understand?

ATTINGER: What do I do?

ADAM: Tell me the truth carefully and accurately.

ATTINGER: Shoot. (*A catch in his throat*) I mean—go ahead.

   ADAM *lights a cigarette.*

ADAM: State your full name.

ATTINGER: Warren Francis Attinger.

ADAM: Where do you reside?

ATTINGER: Sixty-six West Twelfth Street.

ADAM: New York City?

ATTINGER: New York City.

ADAM: Occupation?

Cut to:

[Interior, Corridor—House of Detention
(Women's Prison) (Already Shot in New York)

It is a long, white tile corridor. On one side are four or five cubicles, a little larger than telephone booths, each containing only a table and two chairs. It is in these cubicles that the inmates of the House of Detention are allowed to interview their lawyers. There is a door, with a glass panel in it, on each cubicle, which is kept open. A CORRECTION OFFICER *(woman policeman) sits facing the open door so that she may watch the interview, i.e., to see that no drugs, or anything, are passed to the prisoner. But she is at a sufficient distance so that she cannot overhear the conservation. The atmosphere is antiseptic rather than penal. The swinging door at the end of the corridor opens.* MRS. ATTINGER *enters, accompanied by a* CORRECTION OFFICER. *A* SECOND CORRECTION OFFICER *approaches them.*

SECOND CORRECTION OFFICER *(to* FIRST CORRECTION OFFICER*):* Is this Doris Attinger?

FIRST CORRECTION OFFICER *(nods):* Yes.

SECOND CORRECTION OFFICER *(to* MRS. ATTINGER*):* This way, Doris.

She conducts her to the cubicle nearest the camera. MRS. ATTINGER *follows her, somewhat dazedly, and enters the cubicle. The* CORRECTION OFFICER *crosses the corridor to her chair facing the cubicle, and sits.]*

Cut to:

Interior, Cubicle—the House of Detention—Medium Shot—Grace, Amanda, and Mrs. Attinger

MRS. ATTINGER: Nothing. No occupation.

AMANDA: Housewife.

MRS. ATTINGER: That's right. Housewife.

AMANDA: All right.

MRS. ATTINGER: And mother.

AMANDA: Yes. *(She offers her cigarette case)*

21

MRS. ATTINGER: No thank you. You'll excuse me saying it. I don't believe women should smoke.

AMANDA *nods gravely*.

AMANDA: I'll excuse you.

MRS. ATTINGER: Thank you. It's not feminine.

AMANDA: How long have you been married, Mrs. Attinger?

MRS. ATTINGER: Nine years and four months.

AMANDA: I see.

MRS. ATTINGER: And twelve days.

GRACE *(after a moment)*: Finished?

MRS. ATTINGER: Yes, thank you.

GRACE: Thank *you*.

MRS. ATTINGER: Thank you.

AMANDA: You have three children?

MRS. ATTINGER: Warren, Junior, he's eight. Allan, he's seven. Trudy, she's six. And that's all.

AMANDA: And when did you begin to suspect that you were losing your husband's affection?

MRS. ATTINGER *thinks a moment*.

MRS. ATTINGER: When he started battin' me around.

AMANDA: When was that?

MRS. ATTINGER: Fourteen months ago. March eleventh.

AMANDA: He struck you?

MRS. ATTINGER: The first time, he broke a tooth. *My* tooth.

AMANDA: I see.

MRS. ATTINGER: Upper left molar.

AMANDA: And how often—?

MRS. ATTINGER *(breaking in)*: It's capped now. You can't notice a thing.

AMANDA: Good. Now start with the day of the—accident—and tell us—

MRS. ATTINGER: No accident. I *wanted* to shoot him.

AMANDA: Well, suppose we decide later just what you *wanted* to do.

MRS. ATTINGER: Silly.

AMANDA *(sharply)*: The difference between ten years in prison and freedom isn't silly, Mrs. Attinger. *(See film still 6.)*

MRS. ATTINGER: Call me Doris.

[AMANDA: You follow?][21]

MRS. ATTINGER: I don't care what happens to me.

AMANDA: Do you care what happens to Warren and Allan and Trudy?

MRS. ATTINGER: Yes, I do. *(She begins to cry)* I want to go home. Can't you fix it I should go home?

AMANDA: Not just now, but we're working on it. *(She pours a glass of water and hands it to* MRS. ATTINGER*)* Here.

MRS. ATTINGER: I promised my kids to take 'em in Coney Island tomorrow.

[AMANDA: You'd help us very much if you could reconstruct the day—all of yesterday.][22]

　　MRS. ATTINGER *blows her nose and recovers slightly.*

MRS. ATTINGER: Well—the first thing in the morning—

AMANDA: Yes?

MRS. ATTINGER: I woke up!

AMANDA: Yes?

MRS. ATTINGER: And I saw he didn't sleep home.

　　GRACE *is taking it all down.*

AMANDA: You were shocked and surprised.

MRS. ATTINGER: Oh, no. Not shocked. Not surprised. He used to not do that a lot. Come home.

AMANDA: Did you ever question him about his behavior?

MRS. ATTINGER: Certainly.

AMANDA: Did he offer any explanation?

MRS. ATTINGER: Certainly. He told me to shut up and mind my business.

AMANDA: I see.

---

[21] In the film, instead:
AMANDA: Now, you pay attention to what I'm saying.
[22] In the film, instead:
AMANDA: Yes. You drink that. Now—uh—you would help us very much if you could reconstruct the day—all of yesterday.

MRS. ATTINGER: But [this time]—yesterday—I got worried. No. Not worried. Mad. I got mad. You know why?

AMANDA: Why?

MRS. ATTINGER: Because it was the fourth night in a row he didn't.

AMANDA: Come home.

MRS. ATTINGER: Yuh.

AMANDA: And that made you angry.

MRS. ATTINGER: Sure. It was getting a habit with him. So I sent the kids to school and I went and bought a gun.

AMANDA: Where?

MRS. ATTINGER: This hock shop I go to. I bought a gun and they gave me a book how to. Free.

AMANDA: Had you decided by this time exactly what you planned to do?

Close Shot—Mrs. Attinger

MRS. ATTINGER: I'll tell you the honest truth. I didn't decide nothing. I was just doing everything like in a dream. Like I was watching myself—but I couldn't help it—like a dream.

Close Shot—Amanda

AMANDA: Wait a second. *(She turns)*

Medium Shot

> AMANDA, GRACE *writing swiftly*—MRS. ATTINGER *trancelike now.*

AMANDA *(to GRACE)*: Got all that?

GRACE *(reading her notebook)*: "Like I was watching myself—but I couldn't help it—like a dream."

AMANDA: Good. *(To MRS. ATTINGER)* Go on, Doris.

MRS. ATTINGER: So then I was very hungry.

AMANDA: When?

MRS. ATTINGER: When I bought the gun.

AMANDA: Yuh?

MRS. ATTINGER: So I went in a hamburger place and ate two. Rare. And one lemon meringue pie.

24

AMANDA: Then what?

MRS. ATTINGER: I was still hungry.

GRACE: Think of that.

MRS. ATTINGER: So then I walked all around and I kept talking to myself not to be foolish.

AMANDA: And then?

MRS. ATTINGER: I called up Warren—it was just getting his lunch hour by now and I told him I want to see him important so if we could have lunch together. So he said no, naturally. So I asked him, "Are you coming home after?" So he says, "What for?" So I says, "Don't you live there no more?" So he says, "Don't bother me in the office, you want me to lose my job?" Loud. So then he hung up.

AMANDA: And what did *you* do?

MRS. ATTINGER: I had a cup of coffee.

AMANDA: Where?

MRS. ATTINGER: Same place as him, only he didn't see me. It was crowded. The Buffet Exchange. So then I bought two chocolate nut bars and I went [in his lobby][23] and I waited the whole afternoon and I kept waiting and eating the candy bars till he came out so then I followed him so then I shot him.

AMANDA: And after you shot him, how did you feel then?

A pause as MRS. ATTINGER *searches her soul for the true answer.*

MRS. ATTINGER *(with a touch of embarrassment)*: Hungry.

[Exterior, the Bonner Apartment—Night—Medium Long Shot
A janitor is hosing the front sidewalk.][24]

Interior, the Bonner Dining Room—Full Shot, *across the beautifully set table, through the wide doors leading to the sitting room. The table is set for ten. Flowers, two sets of wine glasses, place cards, the works.* MARY *comes in from the kitchen with*

---

[23] Instead, in the film DORIS says ". . . outside of his office. . . ."
[24] Instead, in the film a title card reads:
THAT EVENING

a trayful of individual salt and pepper holders. She starts to place them. AMANDA *comes in quickly. Her hair is up; she looks stunning, she is mildly distraught. She has not finished dressing. She hands* MARY *a package.*

AMANDA: It's lovely, Mary. You must be dead. *(She goes out and lights the fire)*

MARY: I don't care except the extra help. With me, the more help I got the harder I have to work.

[ADAM's VOICE *(off)*: Hello!

AMANDA *looks at a clock.*

Close Shot—the Clock
It is seven-thirty.][25]

Medium Shot—the Room
AMANDA *starts out;* ADAM *appears in the dining-room doorway; he carries an oddly shaped box.*

[ADAM: Beautiful!][26]

AMANDA *keeps going. As she passes him, they exchange a perfunctory kiss.* ADAM *starts to show the box, but* AMANDA *has left the* SHOT.

Interior, the Sitting Room—Full Shot
AMANDA *comes through, adjusts a flower here, a cigarette box there, on her way upstairs.* ADAM *scurries into the background of the* SHOT, *following her, and gaining, toward* CAMERA.

[ADAM: Look!]

AMANDA *goes up the stairs in a hurry.*

AMANDA *(off)*: Can you dress in four minutes?

[25] In the film, instead:
ADAM *(offscreen)*: Hello. I'm not late, am I?
AMANDA: Isn't that typical?
MARY: Um-hm.
AMANDA: Twenty minutes of eight.
[26] In the film, instead:
ADAM: Ohh, beautiful. Uh—I do—uh—

26

[ADAM *(to himself)*: Can I dress in four minutes? Of course not. *(Shouting up loudly)* Yes, dear, certainly!][27] *(He rushes up)*

Interior, the Bedroom—Full Shot

The bedroom. It is a small room, flanked by a dressing room and a closet, which ADAM *uses as one. The following scene is played in a continuous flow, the* CAMERA *remaining in position. At times the room will be empty, the voices coming from either side. Sometimes* ADAM *will be in, other times* AMANDA, *often both. He will cross to her door, she to his. All this while dressing. Thus, we see them both in many and several stages of dress and undress.*

AMANDA *opens the scene. She enters, takes off her wrapper, and goes out to her dressing room as* ADAM *comes in. He pulls a bench to the center of the room and puts the box on it.*[28] *(See film still 7.) He takes the cover from the box and goes out to his dressing room.*

ADAM: Have a good day?

AMANDA *(offscreen)*: Yes.

ADAM: Make a lot of money?

AMANDA *(offscreen)*: No. Better than money.

ADAM *goes into his dressing room.*

ADAM *(offscreen)*: What?

AMANDA *(offscreen)*: A very interesting development. Very.

ADAM *(offscreen)*: Good.

AMANDA *comes in, wearing a dinner dress. It hangs strangely,*

[27] In the film, instead:
ADAM: Of course, I can't get dressed in four minutes. What do you mean, can I—Why, sure, darling, I can—I can get dressed in four minutes. I—may have a little trouble getting a bath in that time.
[28] In the film:
ADAM: I—uh—uh—
AMANDA *(offscreen)*: You are hurrying up, aren't you, darling? Oh!
ADAM's hands are seen as he takes hat from box. He looks at it and smiles, leans over, and puts hat down.
AMANDA *(offscreen)*: What is Judge Marcasson's wife's name? Do you remember? Oh, I do, I do. Alice. I hope Kip knows enough to behave with the judges around. I'll keep him playing the piano as much as possible.

27

since it is unhooked and unzipped and unsashed. She moves to an open wall safe and starts to get out her jewels.

AMANDA: I hope you'll think so after you've heard what it is—may jar you a bit at first, but—*(She notices the box in the center of the room. She moves to it and brings forth a lovely bonnet. She squeals)* Pinky!

ADAM *(appearing in his doorway)*: Calling me?

AMANDA *(holding the hat aloft)*: What's this?

ADAM *(airily)*: That? Oh, that's just the best hat in the world. *(He goes in, but pops right out again)* For the best head.

He goes back in. AMANDA *follows him in. There are some odd* SOUNDS.

AMANDA *(offscreen)*: [I may snap *your* head off like an old string bean.

ADAM *(offscreen)*: Ow!

AMANDA *(coming out, backward)*: Some day there's going to be a statue of you somewhere.

She begins to try on the hat.][29] *A knock at the door.* ADAM *comes in, tying a tie.*

AMANDA: Yes?

MARY'S VOICE *(offscreen)*: Your mother and father here[, Mr. Bonner].

[ADAM: Be right down.][30]

AMANDA *and* ADAM *dash into their dressing room.*

---

[29] Instead, in the film:
AMANDA: I may ask you to come home late every single night. Ohhh.
ADAM *(offscreen)*: Mmmm.
AMANDA *(offscreen)*: Mmmmm. Hey. *(She enters)* Someday, they're going to build a statue to you somewhere.
ADAM: Huh?
AMANDA: I said—
ADAM: Ohh.
AMANDA: *(trying on the hat)*: Well, now, what about that?
ADAM: That's sweet.
AMANDA: Isn't that absolutely a miracle?
ADAM: Yeah, you look kinda like Grandma Moses.
AMANDA: I'm a lucky girl.
[30] Instead, in the film:
AMANDA: Oh.
ADAM: Oh. All right. Tell 'em we'll be right down.

AMANDA *(offscreen)*: Tell them to fix themselves a drink.

ADAM *(offscreen)*: What?

AMANDA *(offscreen, louder)*: A drink.

ADAM *(offscreen, cheerily)*: No, thank you.

AMANDA *(offscreen)*: What?

> *She comes out of her dressing room, reaching for her back zipper.*

[ADAM's VOICE *(offscreen)*: I said, no, thank you.

AMANDA *(distracted)*: Oh, for the love of—][31]

> *She goes out of the bedroom and on to the landing, the* CAMERA FOLLOWING.

AMANDA: Hello, everybody.

Full Shot, including the cocktail tray in the foreground, and Amanda way up on the landing in the background

> MR. BONNER, SR., *and* MRS. BONNER *sit holding hands.*

MR. BONNER *(shouting)*: Hello, honey.

MRS. BONNER: It's just us, Maddo.

> AMANDA *starts down. In the background we see* ADAM, *hurrying down the stairs.*

ADAM *(from the stairs)*: Good evening, ladies and gentlemen.

[MR. BONNER: Well, son.

MRS. BONNER: Hello, Neddy Boy.

AMANDA *(arriving)*: Sorry to be late, darlings. *(Quite a lot of kissing goes on)* Couldn't help it, though. I've got an irresponsible husband.

---

[31] Instead, in the film:

ADAM: I said, I don't want one, thanks.

AMANDA: Oh, for the love of heaven.

> Interior of the dressing room:

ADAM: How do I look?

AMANDA: Oh, boy, you look handsome. This is a dress I have on.

ADAM: Oh, it's beautiful, beautiful.

> Interior of the lower hall; MARY taking MR. BONNER, SR., and MRS. BONNER's coats:

MARY: They'll be right down, Mrs. Bonner.

BONNER: That's fine—

MRS. BONNER: How are you, Mary?

MARY: Fine.

MRS. BONNER: Hereditary.

AMANDA *(to* ADAM*)*: Adam, would you finish me up back here? *Adam hands a cocktail shaker to his father, who goes to work.* ADAM *puts on his glasses and assists* AMANDA *with the last few unreachable zippers and snaps.*

ADAM *(as he works, with his tongue out of the corner of his mouth)*: Some day, somebody is going to think up something—
MR. BONNER: You've got no complaint.][32] You should have seen some of the things I used to have to handle. Hooks and eyes, begad! She had an evening number once, had about two thousand.
MRS. BONNER: Don't exaggerate.

MR. BONNER: All right, then *one* thousand. Used to start hooking her up, sometimes, right after breakfast.

[KIP LURIE *and* EMERALD *enter.* KIP *is an attractive, bubbling, life-of-the-party type, but lovable. Everybody's for* KIP.
KIP: Look at us, right on time, and all the way from next door!

---

[32] Instead, in the film:
BONNER: Well, son, how are ya'?
ADAM: Dad! Hi!
BONNER: Fine. Fine.
MRS. BONNER: Hello, Adam.
BONNER: Hello, dear.
AMANDA: Adam, go ahead, mix the drinks.
ADAM: Mix the drinks. Come on, Pop.
AMANDA: I'm sorry we're so late—but I'm not to blame. I have an irresponsible husband.
MRS. BONNER: Hereditary.
AMANDA: We're going to have the most sensational dinner. I hope!
MRS. BONNER: Oh?
BONNER: I'll bet—
AMANDA: Oh-oh! My dress! Do it up, w-w-will you, please?
MRS. BONNER: Oh, I'm sorry. I-I-I forgot my glasses.
AMANDA: You did? Oh, well, Adam! Hey, come on in here and fasten me up, will you? Sit down, darling. Sit down—
ADAM: Um? Back? Oh! Here, Pops, you're it. *(He hands Bonner the cocktail shaker)* Mix 'em, don't drink it now. *(He helps Amanda with the last few snaps on the back of the dress)*
BONNER: Oh, yes. Sure.
AMANDA: Go ahead—
ADAM: I s'pose some day somebody will invent something that—
BONNER: You've got no complaint—
AMANDA: Uh, just pull—
ADAM: Yeah, well—

AMANDA: Hello, Kip.

KIP: You know Emerald, don't you? Emerald Messel!

EMERALD: Good evening, everybody.

> *Ad lib hellos.*][33]

KIP: She's been proposing to me. That's why we're on time. *(See film still 8.)*

EMERALD: Ha! Ha!

KIP *(to* MR. BONNER, *indicating Emerald)*: No humor, but stinking rich!

> MR. BONNER *smiles broadly at Emerald—automatically.*

[AMANDA: What to drink, Emerald?][34]

KIP *(to* ADAM*)*: Would you like some help, old friend?

ADAM: No, thanks.

KIP: Why not? She may be your wife—but she's *my* lawyer.

> *General greetings and handshaking. Conventional, until* KIP *comes to* AMANDA. ADAM *is still working on some fasteners.*
>
> KIP *embraces* AMANDA *passionately.*

KIP: Amanda, my only love. Why do you stay married to a legal beagle with ten thumbs?

AMANDA *(pushes him away)*: All right, Kip, that's enough.

---

[33] Instead, in the film:

MARY *(offscreen)*: Good evening.

KIP LURIE *(offscreen)*: Good evening, Mary.

> KIP LURIE and EMERALD MESSEL enter, followed by MARY.

KIP: Anybody else important here yet?

MARY: Good evening—

KIP: Well, look at us, all the way from across the hall and right on time. Don't we look nice?

AMANDA: You certainly do.

KIP: You know Emerald Messel, don't you?

AMANDA: Hello, Emerald. How are you?

KIP: Mrs. Bonner. Bonner.

ADAM: Nice to see you again.

AMANDA: Do you know Adam's father and mother? Emerald Messel.

EMERALD: How do you do?

[34] In the film, instead:

AMANDA: Emerald, what do you want to drink?

EMERALD: Oh, whatever is going.

AMANDA: Dad, would you be an angel?

BONNER: You bet.

AMANDA: Thank you.

KIP: Not for me, it's not.

[ADAM: There!]

>*He finishes the job.*

EMERALD *(to* KIP*)*: Why don't you go play the piano?

KIP: All right. I'm sure that's what I was asked for.[35] Somebody ought to bring me a drink. *(He stops and turns back to the group; then he points, as in a children's game)* I choose Amanda.

>*He continues to the piano.* MR. BONNER *is pouring cocktails, now the remaining four guests are coming into the room.* JUDGE *and* MRS. NATHAN MARCASSON; JUDGE ALAN POYNTER *and his wife,* DOTTY. AMANDA *and* ADAM *start forward to greet them.*

KIP *(to the new arrivals)*: Are you the judges? They said some judges were coming.

[AMANDA: All right, Kip. Hello, Dotty.][36]

KIP *(to* AMANDA*)*: You always have judges here. Why is that? To get in good with them?

[EMERALD: Ha! Ha!

ADAM *(shaking hands)*: How are you, sir? How *very* nice to see you, Mrs. Marcasson.][37]

>ADAM *and* AMANDA *are bringing their guests forward and introducing everyone all around.*

[KIP *(improvising at the piano, and singing)*: How very nice to see you, Mrs. Marcasson!][38]

>*There is the usual activity now, which involves finding places*

---

[35] In the film, ADAM adds, "That's right. That's right."

[36] In the film, instead:

AMANDA: Kip! Hello, darling. How are you?

DOTTY: Hello, dear.

ALL *(ad lib)*: Hello. How are you?

[37] In the film, instead:

ADAM: Well, good evening.

JUDGE MARCASSON: Hello, Adam.

ADAM: And—ah, very nice to see you, Mrs. Marcasson.

[38] In the film:

KIP *(singing)*: How very nice to see you, Mrs. Marcasson.

>How very nice to see you, Mrs. Marcasson.

>The judge is standing by, but I really don't know why.

in and around the room, taking the cocktail orders, and pre-paring them. MR. BONNER *and* ADAM *work hard.*

JUDGE MARCASSON: What were you doing down in my bailiwick today[, Amanda]?

AMANDA: Just a little ambulance chasing.

JUDGE MARCASSON: Successful?

AMANDA: Oh, yes. I got the case.

ADAM *comes over carrying a tray with six cocktails on it.*

ADAM: What case?

JUDGE MARCASSON *takes a cocktail.* ADAM *turns away.*

AMANDA: A lady named Doris Attinger shot her husband. *(*ADAM *stops)* I'm going to defend her.

ADAM *whirls in surprise. The glasses which remain on the tray totter precariously. He makes an effort to balance them by tipping the tray, overshoots his mark, twists it back and forth in a desperate effort, finally succeeds in losing every last glass.*

AMANDA *(continuing)*: [ADAM! Careful!

MRS. BONNER: Oh, dear.

She comes forward to help. MARY *appears in the doorway.*

MARY: Dinner, Madam!][39]

Confusion

Dissolve to:

Interior, Bonner Living Room—Full Shot

An hour or so later. The room is in semidarkness, for ADAM *is showing the guests a few reels of sixteen-mm. home movies. The* ANGLE *is toward the sixteen-mm. screen and over the heads of the spectators.* KIP *is operating the projector.* AMANDA *hovers about replenishing the guests' coffee cups and ducking down to avoid interfering with the throw to the screen. The film is no better, no worse than the average home product.*

---

[39] Instead, in the film:

MARY: Dinner is served, madam.

AMANDA: *(over and above ad libs)*: Uh—Oh, well, let's go on in, everyone. That is—uh—that's all right, darling. Uh—uh—

Some of it is in sharp focus. There is a great deal of panning and shakily held camera work. The speeds are not always constant. The cuts are comparatively short. There is much waving and face-making in the direction of the lens. However, we see that a real effort has been made to string the material into some sort of continuity. The whir of the projector continues throughout. On the screen the shots are the following:[40]

Sixteen-mm. Long Shot—the Lawn, the House, the Great Sugar Maple Tree and the Entrance Gate to Adam's and Amanda's Country Place.

MRS. MARCASSON: Oh! Look at that, will you?

[DOTTY:—ever want to sell, Adam?

AMANDA: Biggest sugar maple in the state, they say.][41]

Sixteen-mm. Extreme Close Shot —outside the Gate

A rustic sign reads: "Bonner Hill"

KIP: How'd you *ever* think of such an *unusual* name? *Your* idea, Adam?

Sixteen-mm. Medium Shot— Road

A small car drives through. As car reaches foreground, JUDGE MARCASSON *waves*

[MR. BONNER: Here comes somebody.

[40] A card "on screen" reads:

Bonner Epics
Present
"THE MORTGAGE THE MERRIER"
A Too Real Epic

KIP (*offscreen*): The trouble with this picture—it drags.
AMANDA (*offscreen*): Shut up, Kip. Are you all sure that you want to see this?
KIP: I don't.
[41] In the film, instead:
AMANDA (*offscreen*): Oh, this is our main house. The cottage is out here by the camera.
KIP (*offscreen*): I can't see it.

with hat and calls "Hello"—
drives off.

Interior, the Room—Close Shot

JUDGE MARCASSON. *He is watching the screen. He is pleased to see himself.*

JUDGE MARCASSON: Who's that handsome chap?
He laughs. The room follows suit, politely.]

Medium Shot—the Sixteen-mm. Screen

We are closer to it than before.

Sixteen-mm. Shot—Tennis Court

AMANDA *in sweater and shorts playing tennis—sees* JUDGE's *car offscene—exits.*

EMERALD: Cute outfit, Amanda. *Really* cute.
KIP *(after a wolfish whistle)*: Mighty pretty country up there.[42]
EMERALD: Ha-ha—
KIP: I knew a lady once collapsed a lung laughing like that.

Sixteen-mm. Medium Long Shot

Section of garden with lawn furniture. AMANDA *enters through a hedge—does some very amateurish acting (deliberate) indicating she is awaiting the judge.*

KIP *(to* EMERALD *as though she had addressed him)*: What! Yes, she *does* remind me of Fatty Arbuckle.
EMERALD: I didn't say anything, Maddo. Honestly.
KIP: A sterling piece of acting, I call it. What do you call it?
MR. BONNER *(sincerely)*: You ought to be on the stage, Maddo.
KIP: Yes—anywhere but in this picture.]

---

[42] In the film, AMANDA says, "Thank you."

AMANDA *notices* ADAM *asleep on lounge in foreground. She stops sixteen-mm. acting. She awakens him—*

TITLE *(home-movie style)*: "Wake up—company coming!!" *—he doesn't like being disturbed while napping. She tells him he's ruining the movie—calls his attention to camera—he gestures to camera, "Stop that crap." She calls his attention to* JUDGE's *car approaching on road, background. Car stops,* JUDGE MARCASSON *gets out.* ADAM *gets up from lounge, doesn't realize his trousers are unbuttoned—almost loses them as he and* AMANDA *start off to greet the* JUDGE. *Big welcoming scene, all self-conscious. (See film still 9.)*

KIP: Cute outfit, Adam—*really* cute.

Sixteen-mm. Close Shot—Edge of Pool
ADAM *playing with two dogs.*

AMANDA: Oh, look at those darling dogs.
KIP *(counting deliberately)*: One —two—three—

Sixteen-mm. Close Shot—Lawn
[AMANDA *tries to ride a small wobbly hobbyhorse— she falls off, gets on, falls off*

again, poses on her knees with arm around its neck.]

[AMANDA: Now me and *my* pet. Fair's fair.]

KIP: Sort of an animal picture, isn't it?

Sixteen-mm. Medium Shot—on Another Part of the Property
Table laid out for lunch at one side, portable barbecue nearby and between the two a large tree. JUDGE, ADAM, *and* AMANDA *are standing in front of the lunch table, the two dogs at their feet.* JUDGE MARCASSON *has changed to sports clothes, which makes the cut seem awkward, to say the least. The three of them are posed at the lunch table, waiting for the camera to grind. The minute it does they spring into very false action.*

[KIP: Do you think silent pictures will ever come back?][43]

JUDGE *takes the mortgage out of his pocket, holds it up.*

EMERALD: What's that, anyway?
AMANDA: The mortgage.
JUDGE MARCASSON: That was the day they paid off the mortgage. Brought it out myself.

---

[43] In the film, instead:
BONNER: Oh, now—
AMANDA: Kip!
KIP: I would say this movie has a rather limited appeal.

ADAM *brings forth a check.*
He comes up close to camera, AMANDA: Yes.
holding the check up in front
of him for close shot of check. KIP: Looks like rubber from
here.

Then he returns to JUDGE
and AMANDA. JUDGE *hands*
him a pen. AMANDA *leans* JUDGE MARCASSON: We acted
over and, using her back as all this out after, though. I
a desk, ADAM *affixes his* mean it isn't actual.
signature to the check. He
then hands her the check and KIP: All right, big mouth, settle
fountain pen. He bends over down.
and she repeats the action,
using his back. AMANDA: Kip!
KIP: [Who took these pictures,
your cow?][44]
[JUDGE MARCASSON: Historic
moment.
KIP: Actual!]

Medium Shot—in the Room—Adam

He is not *watching the screen. He is troubled and glum.*
AMANDA'*s face comes into the* SHOT. *She whispers something*
into his ear. His expression does not change a bit.

Medium Close Shot—the Screen Again, *nothing in the foreground.*

Sixteen-mm. Medium Shot

ADAM *reaches for mort-*
*gage—*JUDGE *withholds it—*
holds out hand for check.

---

[44] In the film, instead:
KIP: Seems much slower that the other eight times I've seen it— Who took
these pictures, your cow?

Horseplay between ADAM *and* JUDGE *and* AMANDA *as they exchange check for document.*
[TITLE: "CONGRATULATIONS!"][45]

ADAM *and* AMANDA *rush to portable barbecue, stick the mortgage into the barbecue.* ADAM *uses the flame of the burning mortgage to toast some hotdogs, amid great hilarity. Then they rush to tree.*[47]

[JUDGE MARCASSON: You own it all now—lock, stock and leaky plumbing.][46]

MR. BONNER, SR.: You should have taken a picture of burning it up. The mortgage. That would've been a good one.

AMANDA: We did! Wait and see.

Sixteen-mm. Medium Shot—at Huge Tree
ADAM *and* AMANDA *each embrace it, kissing its trunk.*

KIP *(à la James Fitzpatrick)*: Tree-kissing. A famous old Connecticut custom.

Sixteen-mm. Medium Long Shot —the Barn
A cow is seen in the background; a horse and its foal in foreground.[48] ADAM *and*

[45] In the film, the title reads:
CONGRATULATIONS!
You Own It All
Now, Lock, Stock,
and Leaky Plumbing!
[46] In the film, instead:
BONNER: You oughta be on the stage, Judge.
KIP: Yeah. Anywhere but in this picture.
[47] While this is on screen, KIP says, "Oh-ho! Cute, Adam. Very cute."
MRS. MARCASSON: Oh, expensive hot dogs.
BONNER: Our tree.

AMANDA *come into the shot,*
walk up the ramp of the barn,
kiss the barn door. Door
swings slightly open—ADAM
pushes AMANDA *into barn*   KIP: Barn kissing. A famous
and pretends to lock her in.   old Connecticut custom.
He leers at the camera.
AMANDA *sticks her head out*
of door holding some hay as
a mustache (this is just kill-
ing). Then ADAM *pushes her*
back into the barn, and with
another horrendous leer, fol-
lows in after her, locking the
door.[49]

TITLE:

"CENSORED"

Sixteen-mm. Medium Shot—
River

ADAM *and* AMANDA *in ca-*
noe. (See film still 10.) [*He*
is paddling. She lies on
canoe bottom, her head in

---

[48] While this is on screen, JUDGE MARCASSON says, "See the arrow on the horse?"
EMERALD: Oh, yes.
BONNER: Yes.
[49] While this is on screen:
KIP (*over and above offscreen laughter*): What a funny funny. Oh-ho. It's so—
BONNER: Oh!
  KIP whistles and stomps his feet; AMANDA and the others laugh.
KIP: Whoo!
EMERALD: Oh, that's wonderful.

*his lap. He bends over and
kisses her, then sprinkles
water on her. She rocks the
boat.]*[50]

KIP: Wife-kissing. A famous
old Connecticut custom.

Sixteen-mm. Medium Shot
*The canoe in the water,
upside-down.*[51]

KIP *(jumps up)*: All right,
everybody—on your heads. *(He
stands on his head on a chair)*[52]

Sixteen-mm. Medium Long Shot
*The canoe as it goes under
bridge.*

[TITLE:
"THAT'S ALL, EVERYBODY."
GOOD NIGHT."]

[KIP: And so, as the sunking
sin sank into the sitting soo, we
say, "Farewell to Bonner Hill
and to these sickening home
movies."][53]

Dissolve to:
Interior, the Bedroom—Full Shot
*The setup here should duplicate the previous bedroom scene.
The action should duplicate the scene, but in reverse (not to*

---

[50] In the film, they are both paddling. While this is on screen:
ALL *(ad lib)*: Oh, isn't that pretty? Beautiful, beautiful.
[51] While this is on screen:
ALL *(ad lib)*: Oh-oh. Upsy-daisy.
[52] In the film:
BONNER: What a clown.
[53] Instead, in the film:
KIP: And, as the sanking soo sunks into the sinking sand, we say,
"Good-by . . .
   All applaud as KIP turns off movie projection machine.
KIP: ". . . to Bonner Hill and the sickening home movies."
ALL *(ad lib)*: Wonderful, Maddo. Very good.

the extent of the standard sport shot of return-to-the-diving board, but almost). The room is empty as we complete the dissolve.

AMANDA'S VOICE *(offscreen, raised to carry across the bedroom to* ADAM'S *dressing room)*: All right, all right, all right! *(She comes into the room in her dressing gown, removing her jewelry)* You've said the same thing nine times.

ADAM'S VOICE *(offscreen, likewise raised)*: Time number ten, then. *(He strides into the room in his shirt sleeves, pantless, still yelling. As he sees* AMANDA *his voice drops to normal volume without missing a beat)* Amanda, please lay off this Attinger thing. Will you?

AMANDA: Did you have to sulk all evening?

ADAM: Now, wait—

AMANDA: —with a growl on your face.

She goes back into her dressing room.

ADAM: How can a man have a growl on his—If you think you're going to turn this case into a Punch and Judy show—

AMANDA *comes in and puts out a light.*

[AMANDA: Adam—be fair. This means a great deal to me.][54]

ADAM: Would you—

AMANDA *(continuing)*: It's not a stunt. This woman—isn't she entitled to the same justice—I mean, that's usually reserved for men? Sure, the same unwritten law that got Lennahan off.

ADAM: —let me—

AMANDA *(gaining fire)*: I know what you're going to say. That he should have been convicted too. Well, he wasn't, was he?

ADAM: —get a word in—

AMANDA: And you're not going to put this poor thing away just because she had the misfortune to be born a female. Not if I can help it.

ADAM: —edgewise?

---

[54] In the film, instead:
AMANDA: Darling, please, please—
ADAM: —I want to tell you, you don't—
AMANDA: —This means a great deal to me.

AMANDA *(impatiently)*: What?

ADAM *(fast as he can go)*: Wouldyouletmegetawordinedgewise?

AMANDA *(magnanimously)*: Go ahead.

ADAM *(his anger at white heat)*: Not one sybbalul—syllable—

AMANDA *(quietly)*: You're too excited.

ADAM: —of what you've just blabbered—

AMANDA: That always happens when you get too excited.

A pause. She picks up the clock and begins winding it.

ADAM *(slowly)*: I'm going to cut you up into twelve little pieces and feed you to the jury. So brace yourself!

She finishes winding the clock. They're standing between the beds now. She drops her dressing gown. He his robe. They're in their night clothes.

AMANDA *(very softly)*: Good night, Pinky.

ADAM *(softer still)*: Good night[, Pinkie].

She embraces him and they kiss. They're still at it, as we

Dissolve to:

Exterior, Court of General Sessions

The facade, featuring the chiseled Jefferson Inscription:
> "Equal and exact justice to all men
> Of whatever state or persuasion."

Dissolve to:

Interior, General Sessions—the Courtroom

The courtroom, early in the morning of this first day, is far from crowded. A handful of people dot the benches.

We are assuming that this is a Calendar Part. The JUDGE *is already seated on the bench. He is accepting papers from two attorneys who have just finished an argument at the bench on a motion which he is taking under submission. There are about forty prospective jurors sitting in the first two rows of the spectators' benches.*

(To the above, add witnesses to the general audience and add attorneys inside the rail.)

ADAM *has just moved over to the counsel table on the*

JUDGE's *right, where his three assistants (two male, one female) are seated. All are busily arranging their papers, etc.*

JUDGE *(to the two attorneys)*: Very well, gentlemen. I will take it under submission. *(Looking at an Assistant D.A. and a defending attorney who are seated inside the railing)* Have you agreed on a date for People Versus [Jones]?

AMANDA, *with* GRACE *and a bright young man from her office (who have been sitting inside the rail) take their places at the other table. This should give the impression of two prizefighters with their trainers, etc., entering the ring for battle.*

The ASSISTANT D.A. *and the attorney addressed both rise and approach the bench.*

Medium Shot
The door from the pen opens. A CORRECTION OFFICER *and* MRS. ATTINGER *start in.*

ASSISTANT D.A. *(as he approaches)*: Yes, Your Honor [the thirtieth].

Close Shot—Adam, *at his table. He gulps.*

The JUDGE *and the* CLERK *note this date on their respective calendars.*

Medium Shot—from Adam's Angle
Somehow the COURT ATTENDANT *and the* CORRECTION OFFICER *screen* MRS. ATTINGER *so that she is hidden from sight entirely, but her hat is not. Or rather* AMANDA's *hat! The hat that* ADAM *gave her the other day. Yes. It moves along now, confident and tasteful on* MRS. ATTINGER's *head.*

A COURT ATTENDANT *approaches the bench, and in a low voice addresses the* JUDGE.

Close Shot—Adam, *furious. He looks over toward* AMANDA.

COURT ATTENDANT: Part Three is available for assignment, Your Honor.

Close Shot—Amanda, *watching happily.*

JUDGE: Very well. *(Then, looking at his calendar, he announces)* People versus [Smith][55] is assigned to Part Three. All witnesses in that case will proceed to that part.

   Following this, a number of people—the witnesses in that case in the audience and the attorneys in that case inside the rail—rise and proceed toward the door leading from the courtroom.

Medium Shot

   The room. ADAM *and* AMANDA *exchange a long and meaningful look.*

   MRS. ATTINGER *is seated.*

Medium Shot—the Bench

   The courtroom generally quiets down as the CLERK *raps for order, following a nod from the* JUDGE.

[JUDGE *(to* ADAM *and* AMANDA*)*: You may proceed.][56]

ADAM: Your Honor, I move the case of the People of the State of New York versus Doris Szabo Attinger for trial.

JUDGE: Is the defendant ready?

AMANDA: Defendant's ready.

JUDGE: Very well. You may proceed to select a jury.

   The CLERK *hands indictment and papers to the* JUDGE.

---

[55] In the film, the name is Delwyn.
[56] In the film, instead:
JUDGE REISER: The People against Attinger. You may proceed.

The CLERK *deposits the jury ballots in jury wheel and spins wheel. He draws ballot from wheel and calls:*

CLERK: Paul Hurlock!

A man from the jury portion of the audience rises and approaches toward CLERK *at witness stand.*[57] *As* HURLOCK *nears him, the* CLERK *extends the Bible to him.*

CLERK: Place your left hand on the Bible and raise your right hand.

HURLOCK *does so.*

CLERK: You do solemnly swear that you will true answers make to all questions put to you upon the several challenges touching upon your competency as a fair and impartial Juror in this proceeding between the People of the State of New York and Doris Szabo Attinger, so help you God?

HURLOCK: I do!

CLERK *(indicating witness box)*: Be seated and state your full name and address.

HURLOCK: Paul Hurlock. 1731 Boylston Avenue, New York City.

This information is noted by the CLERK *and the stenographer.*

Full Shot—the Room

ADAM *approaches the witness box and begins his examination—as* CLERK *inserts slip in jury panel board and hands it to* ADAM.

ADAM *(puzzled)*: Mr. Hurlock, your occupation is . . . ?

HURLOCK: Infant's headgear.

[ADAM: Have you ever served on a jury before?

HURLOCK: Twice. Twice they got me.]

ADAM: Are you personally acquainted with one Warren Attinger?

HURLOCK: No.

ADAM: With Doris Szabo Attinger?

HURLOCK: No.

ADAM: Beryl Caighn?

HURLOCK: No.

ADAM: Do you believe that you are able to render a fair and

---

[57] In the film, HURLOCK rises and starts to put his coat on his seat, but an officer tells him, "Take your coat with you, please." He does so.

honest verdict in this case, based upon the evidence adduced and the law as laid down by the Court?

HURLOCK: Sure.

ADAM: Yes?

HURLOCK: Yes.

ADAM: The juror is acceptable to the People.

He moves back to his place, as AMANDA *rises.*

AMANDA: Good morning, Mr. Hurlock.

HURLOCK: Good morning.

AMANDA *(suddenly)*: Do you believe in equal rights for women?

HURLOCK: What?

ADAM *(on his feet, swiftly)*: Objection!

AMANDA: May it please the Court, I submit that my entire line of defense is based upon the proposition that persons of the female sex should be dealt with, before the law, as the equals of persons of the male sex. I submit that I cannot hope to argue this line before minds hostile to and prejudiced against the female sex.

ADAM: Your Honor, the objection stands.

THE JUDGE: 'V'ruled.

ADAM: Exception.

THE JUDGE: 'Peat y'r questch, couns.

AMANDA *(to Hurlock)*: Do you believe in equal rights for women?

HURLOCK: I should say not.

[AMANDA: Does that mean that your answer is no?

HURLOCK: That's right. No. Yes.

AMANDA: You do *not* believe in equal rights for women?

HURLOCK: I do not.]

AMANDA: The defendant challenges this juror for cause.

THE JUDGE *(to Hurlock)*: Excused.

> HURLOCK *leaves the stand and the courtroom.*

THE CLERK: Benjamin Klausner!

A man rises and comes forward.

Medium Close Shot—Adam

He drums the table with the eraser of his pencil. Softly and deliberately. He looks over at AMANDA.

Medium Close Shot—Amanda

She is studying her jury panel board. She looks up at the prospective juror who has just reached the box.

Close Shot—Adam, *still looking at* AMANDA. *He drums a little louder.*

Close Shot—Amanda

She looks over at ADAM.

Close Shot—Adam.

He stops drumming, carefuly places the pencil on the edge of the table, and with the middle finger of his right hand, knocks it off. He looks at KLAUSNER *with feigned interest.*

Close Shot—Amanda

She smiles, almost imperceptibly, then places her pencil at the table's edge.

Close Shot—Adam

He nods, then bends down under the table.

Close Shot—Amanda

She knocks her pencil off and bends down.

Full Shot—the Room

ADAM *and* AMANDA *are down under.*

Medium Shot

Across ADAM'S *upside-down head in the foreground we see* AMANDA'S *upside-down head surrounded by an odd assortment of feet and legs belonging to furniture and humans. She smiles an upside-down smile.*

Medium Shot—Reverse of the Above

ADAM *smiles back and kisses the air in her direction.*

Medium Shot—Reverse of the Above

AMANDA *echoes the action.*

During the above, we hear the CLERK's *voice.*[58]

[CLERK's VOICE *(offscreen)*: You are Benjamin Klausner—

KLAUSNER's VOICE *(offscreen, correcting the pronunciation)*: *KLAWS*-ner.

CLERK's VOICE *(offscreen)*: —Klausner, of 107 E. Seventy-seventh Street, New York City?

KLAUSNER's VOICE *(offscreen)*: I am.]

CLERK's VOICE *(offscreen)*: Place your left hand on the Bible and raise your right hand. *(A pause)* You do solemnly swear that you will true answers make to all questions put to you upon the several challenges touching upon your competency as a fair and impartial Juror in this proceeding between the People of the State of New York and Doris Szabo Attinger, so help you God?

KLAUSNER's VOICE *(offscreen)*: I do!

CLERK's VOICE *(offscreen)*: Be seated.[59]

Full Shot—the Room

As ADAM *and* AMANDA *come up,* ADAM *rises and moves toward the witness stand. He is frustrated. He has forgotten the jury panel board as he reaches for it.*

[ADAM: Your occupation, Mr. Klausner, is . . .?]

KLAUSNER: Projectionist. Motion-picture projectionist.

ADAM: Have you ever served on a motion-picture projectionist before?

KLAUSNER *(confused)*: What?

The JUDGE *and the* CLERK *look at* ADAM *in mild surprise.*

---

[58] In the film, the CLERK first says, "Your Honor, in view of the fact that counsel have agreed that alternate jurors are not to be selected, may we proceed without making a call for additional prospective jurors at this time?"
JUDGE REISER *(offscreen)*:You may proceed.
[59] In the film, the CLERK continues: "You're Benjamin Klausner?"
KLAUSNER: *KLAWS*-ner.
CLERK: State your address.
KLAUSNER: 107 East Seventy-seventh Street, New York City.
CLERK: Occupation?

ADAM: What? Oh. I mean—have you ever served on a jury before?

AMANDA *laughs,* ADAM *looks at her with some annoyance.*[60]

Dissolve to:

[Exterior, along the East River at Gracie Square—Evening—Long Shot

There's a quiet time in the city's life, when it pauses between work and play. This is it. The lights are just coming on.][61]

Dissolve to:

Interior, the Sitting Room of the Bonner Apartment—Full Shot

The lamp-lit sitting room, with AMANDA *on a sofa. She is reading the evening papers. Beside her, on the table, is a tray of cocktail ingredients and a half-filled glass cocktail shaker.* ADAM *enters from the hallway, calling:*

ADAM: Hello, thing.

AMANDA: Hello, at last.

ADAM *leaves his hat in the hallway, comes forward and finds room for himself, somehow, on the sofa.*

ADAM: Well well well.

AMANDA: Well well well what?

ADAM: Here we are.

AMANDA: How true!

ADAM: [Home was never like this!][62]

AMANDA: You took the words right out. *(He heaves a weary sigh)* Darling—

ADAM *(absently—looking off)*: Mmmmmm—mh?

AMANDA: Are you all right?

[ADAM: In what way?][63]

AMANDA: In health—and so forth.

ADAM: Sure.

---

[60] KLAUSNER is heard saying, "No."
[61] Instead, a title reads:
THAT EVENING.
[62] In the film he says, "Home at last."
[63] In the film he says, "How do you mean?"

50

AMANDA: Oh good—*(goes back to reading papers)*

ADAM: In health, splendid. In so forth—fair. *(Indicating the shaker)* What's this some of?

AMANDA: Some of daiquiris.

ADAM: Good.

He pours himself a drink, takes a sip.

AMANDA *(reading)*: Nobody died in the evening papers. Isn't that nice?

ADAM: Why is it that—is it the perverseness of human nature or what?

ADAM: What?

ADAM: Every night when Mary's off in the night, I feel like staying home. And vice-versa.

AMANDA: Not me. I love going out to dinner. Rather go out than anything.

ADAM: Where would you like to go tonight?

AMANDA: No place. Like to stay home tonight. Would you mind?

ADAM: What?!

AMANDA *(begging)*: Please—

[ADAM: Sure.][64]

AMANDA: Cook something up ourselves. Something exotic. How would you care for some of that?

ADAM: I would.

AMANDA: Of what?

ADAM: What you said.

AMANDA *(still reading)*: Oh, fine. You going to make it?

ADAM: What? Listen, you're not making any sense at all. Do you want to talk to me or read the papers?

AMANDA: Read the papers.

ADAM: Why?

AMANDA *(looking at him)*: Quite a lot about *me* in them, I guess that's why.

ADAM: I'll bet.

[64] In the film, instead:
ADAM: Well, I don't know. All right. All right.

AMANDA *(back to her papers)*: You feel Pinky, cranky?

ADAM: Huh?

AMANDA: I mean—you feel cranky, Pinky?

[ADAM: A little.

AMANDA: Hard day, huh?

ADAM: Not so bad.][65]

AMANDA: Court all day, were you?

ADAM: Yuh.

AMANDA: Had to mix it up with a tough customer, I'll bet. That always makes you a little irritable.

[ADAM: No, nothing like that. In fact, a cinch.

AMANDA: Nothing to it, huh?

ADAM: Next to nothing.

AMANDA: Well, *that's* good, isn't it?

ADAM: Isn't it.

AMANDA *(stops reading—they look at each other)*: Yes.][66]

ADAM: Dear—

AMANDA: You mean me?

ADAM: Sure thing. Now listen—

AMANDA: I'm all ears.

ADAM: I wish you were.

AMANDA: What?

ADAM: Are you all right?

AMANDA: Of course, why?

ADAM: Nothing, I just wouldn't ever want you to be—not all right, that's all.

AMANDA *(out of the tension)*: You know what you are—

ADAM: What?

AMANDA: Lovable!

[65] In the film, instead:
ADAM: Mm.
AMANDA: Hard day, huh?
ADAM: Mm.
[66] In the film, instead:
ADAM: Not so bad. Not so bad. As a matter of fact, it was a cinch.
AMANDA: Well, that's good, isn't it?
ADAM: Mm. Isn't it?
AMANDA: Oh, my, my, my.

52

ADAM: I know it.

AMANDA: You hungry? I'm hungry.

[ADAM: Let's go.][67]

> They untangle, kiss each other, and start for the kitchen, the CAMERA FOLLOWING. ADAM reaches out and touches the back of AMANDA's head.

Interior, the Bonner Kitchen—Full Shot

> Across the kitchen, which is dark, into the hall and sitting room, both lighted. ADAM and AMANDA come toward CAMERA. ADAM is massaging the back of her neck.

AMANDA (rolling her head): Oh, thank you! Thank you from the bottom of my heart.

ADAM: Give you a real rubdown later. (He switches off the sitting-room lights) If you give me one.

AMANDA: Yes.

> He swings her around and grabs her; they disappear from the CAMERA's VIEW.

ADAM's VOICE: More like it.

AMANDA's VOICE: Ouch!

ADAM's VOICE: What's the matter?

AMANDA's VOICE: Mmmmm!

[ADAM's VOICE (a whisper): That's the kind I like. Soft centers.]

> A squeal from AMANDA, followed by a cry of shocked and angry outrage.

[AMANDA's VOICE: Adam!]

> Now she swings around the doorway and into the SHOT. She hits the kitchen switch and we see a great, lovely, sweet grin on her face which belies the sound she has just uttered. She moves past the CAMERA, out of the SHOT. We hear a refrigerator door open. Now, a hand comes around the door jamb and knocks—followed by ADAM's head. The great lipstick print on his face makes it appear as though he is the possessor of two mouths, one at right angles to the other.

[67] In the film, instead:

ADAM: Yes, I'm starving. Let's go.

53

ADAM: [Spare] anything for a hungry man?

Medium Shot—Amanda, *at the icebox.*
AMANDA: [There's some] cheese. Soufflé, maybe?

Medium Shot—Adam, *as he moves across to join her.*
ADAM: I've got enough on my mind without a soufflé.
   He has joined her now in a:

Two-Shot—Amanda and Adam
ADAM: Ought to be some lamb left over, no?
AMANDA *(looking)*: No. No, I don't think—wait a minute—yes!
[ADAM: Curry. Lamb curry, okay?][68]
AMANDA: Perfect. Rice.
ADAM: Any chutney?
AMANDA: I think so.
ADAM: Tea. Tea with curry is the thing.
AMANDA: The thing. And salad.
   They set to work with the spirit and joy of true gourmets—as
   though competing for the Cordon Bleu. They move about the
   small, perfect kitchen as they work. And as they work, they
   talk. ADAM *sets the alcove table and prepares a salad*
   expertly. AMANDA *dons an apron and concentrates on the rice,*
   and lamb curry. (See film still 11.) The Bonner kitchen is the
   sort of kitchen you would expect the Bonners to have. Small,
   and neat. Well equipped. Copper pots and pans. A huge herb
   stand. And over to one side an alcove for dining. A kitchen you
   can live in.
[ADAM: You were pretty cute in there today, my little.][69]
AMANDA: Not so bad yourself, chum.

---

[68] In the film, instead:
ADAM: Lamb?
AMANDA: Um-hm.
ADAM: Curry. Lamb curry. What do you say?
[69] In the film, instead:
ADAM: Give me the junk for the salad. Hey, do you know—you were
pretty cute in there today, my little?

I

2

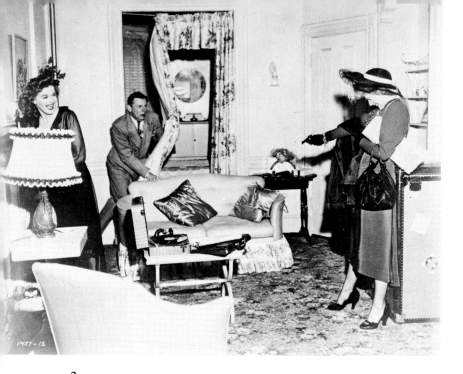

3

4

5

6

7

8

9

10

11

12

13

14

15

16

17

18

19

20

21

22

23

24

25

26

27

She stops as she begins to measure the curry powder. There is a little silence.

ADAM *(salad bowl in hand)*: Mind a bit of the old garlic?

AMANDA: Why a bit?

ADAM *is working expertly on the salad.*

ADAM: Pinkie.

AMANDA: What, Pinky?

ADAM: Do me a favor?

AMANDA: Not too much salt?

ADAM: No. Give up the case?

AMANDA: I can't.

ADAM: [Why? I mean,] why not?

AMANDA: It's my cause.

ADAM: I know, but—

[AMANDA: You want to wash this, like a good kid?

She hands him a sauce beater. He washes it.]

ADAM: I could tell, just from today, this is going to get messier and sillier day by day by day.

AMANDA: By day.

ADAM: I don't ask many favors.

AMANDA: Sure you do.

ADAM: You could handle it from your desk—

AMANDA: Not as good.

ADAM: Practically.

AMANDA: Listen, Adam. I know that deep down you agree with me —with all I believe and want and hope for. We couldn't be so close if you didn't. If I didn't feel you did.

ADAM: Sure.

AMANDA: Now, this trial. Sure, maybe it has a little of the inconvenience of the spotlight, but that's my whole point.

ADAM: What is?

AMANDA: Don't put any green peppers in. Indigestible.

ADAM: Everything's indigestible to somebody.

AMANDA: Anyway, I don't like green peppers.

ADAM: All right.

AMANDA: Take the Boston Tea Party.

ADAM: Instead of peppers?

AMANDA: What did they do? Dramatized an injustice. And that's all *I'm* doing.

ADAM: First thing you know there'll be jokes about us on the radio.

AMANDA: All in a good cause.

ADAM: Your cause.

AMANDA *(seriously)*: Everybody's. [You forgot the teacups.]

> ADAM *has, during the foregoing, attended to the sundries, and a first course.* AMANDA *sits.* ADAM *sits. They are about to begin their melon when the door buzzer sounds—long and loud.*

ADAM: Listen, now, there's just enough for two.

> *He goes out.* AMANDA *gets up, looks in a mirror, refreshes her lip make-up. She stirs the curry.*

KIP's VOICE *(offscreen)*: Hello, you well-known thing you.

ADAM's VOICE *(offscreen)*: How are you?

> *We see them approaching.*

KIP: You don't really care. You just ask because you can't think of anything else to say.

> *They have reached the kitchen by now.* AMANDA *has resumed her seat.*

KIP: You don't care if I live or die.

> KIP *is dressed in white tie and tails and carries a coat. Also a full set of the evening papers.*

KIP *(to* AMANDA*)*: Hello, lawyer dear. You seen all these?

AMANDA: Yes, thank you.

KIP: Oh. Well, have some extras. Marvelous goings-on all right. Everybody's talking about it. *(See film still 12.)*

AMANDA: That's the idea.

KIP: Sort of like the World Series, sort of, isn't it?

ADAM: I'm afraid so.

KIP *(looking at* ADAM*)*: What are you eating? Raspberry jam? *(He looks closer)* Or AMANDA's face?

ADAM: What?

> *He pulls out a handkerchief and wipes his lips. He is greatly*

miffed, particularly since KIP *and* AMANDA *choose to laugh it up rather boisterously.* ADAM *goes back to his place in the alcove and tries to eat his dinner as nonchalantly as possible.*

ADAM *(muttering)*: Very funny.

[AMANDA *(indicating* KIP*)*: No, it was just when he—]

ADAM: [All right, all right, all right.] *(*AMANDA *stops laughing)* You could have—

AMANDA: I didn't even notice the—

ADAM: Well, maybe if you looked at me once in a while you'd see that—

KIP: Oh, bicker bicker bicker. *(To an imaginary companion)* I give them three months at the most.

ADAM *slams down his fork.*

ADAM *(to Kip)*: [Listen.] What do you want around here anyway?

KIP *(coyly)*: As if you don't know! *(He moons at* AMANDA*)*

AMANDA: How's it coming, Kip?

KIP: The show?

AMANDA: Yes.

KIP: Smashing, smashing. Couldn't work much today, though. Another notion got in the way.[70] A new song. Want to hear it? It's not finished but still—

AMANDA: Well—*(She looks at the fuming* ADAM*)* Some other time.

KIP: [Take a minute.] Please. It's for you. And Adam—you don't have to listen.

He dashes out. There is a violent pantomimic exchange between AMANDA *and* ADAM. AMANDA *serves the curry.*[71]

KIP's VOICE: Listening? *(He runs a fancy arpeggio)*

Interior, the Sitting Room—Medium Shot

KIP *at the piano. He sings and accompanies himself sympathetically. It's a lovely tune.*

---

[70] At this point, AMANDA says, "Oh? What?"

[71] In the film:

ADAM: Written a song?

AMANDA: Darling, don't be so cross. He really—he's sweet.

57

KIP *(singing)*:
Farewell, Amanda,
Adios, addio, adieu—*

Interior, the Kitchen—Medium Shot—Amanda and Adam
*He is dumfounded at the guy's gall. She is embarrassed, but
also a little pleased. He looks at her, she turns away. She peeks
at him, he begins to eat, furiously. Meanwhile—the song goes
on.*
KIP's VOICE *(singing)*:
Farewell, Amanda,
It all was great fun—*

Interior, the Sitting Room—Close Shot—Kip
KIP *(singing)*:
But it's done
It's through.
Still now and then,
Fair Amanda—*(He sings romantically these words to his tune)*
[Now comes the middle part
Ta-da-
It needs some work in here
Pa-pa-pa-*pa*!]
When you're stepping on
The stars above
Please recall that wonderful night
On the veranda—*

Interior, the Kitchen—Medium Shot—Amanda and Adam
Both concentrating on food now. KIP's *song goes on.*
[AMANDA: Wonderful, this salad.
ADAM *(a whisper)*: Thank you.]

* "Farewell Amanda," words and music by Cole Porter. Copyright 1949.
Reprinted by permission of the publisher, T.B. Harms Company.

58

KIP'S VOICE:

Sweet Amanda

And our love.[72]

A pause, then KIP *appears modestly.*

KIP: Did I hear someone say, "Sing it again"?[73]

AMANDA: It's pretty.

ADAM: Yes. Pretty fresh.

KIP: You're not friendly to me. I may consult my lawyer.

AMANDA: I think you ought to change the name.

KIP: Can't. It won't scan, see?

[ADAM *(to* AMANDA*)*: Tea now?

AMANDA: Yes, please.

ADAM: There's some strawberries.

AMANDA *(to* KIP*)*: Our own. From the farm.

A pause.

KIP: It won't scan. *(Another pause)*] Well. Good luck tomorrow,

---

[72] At this point, KIP stops singing and says, "No verse yet." The camera cuts back to ADAM and AMANDA in the kitchen, and KIP says offscreen: "Listening? Listening?" and resumes singing:

> Farewell, Amanda,
> Adios, addio, adieu . . . .

The camera returns to KIP singing and playing in the living room:

> Farewell, Amanda,
> It all was great fun
> But it's done
> It's through.
> Still now and then,
> Fair Amanda,
> When you're stepping on
> The stars above
> Please recall that wonderful night
> On the veranda,
> Sweet Amanda . . .*

* "Farewell Amanda," words and music by Cole Porter. Copyright 1949. Reprinted by permission of the publisher, T.B. Harms Company.

The camera returns to the kitchen, where ADAM is seated at the table and AMANDA is standing at the door and whistling as KIP sings offscreen: ". . . and our love." ADAM swings the door closed in a fury. The door hits AMANDA in the back, and she yells, "Help!" The door swings back and hits ADAM, who yells, "Ow." "Pardon," AMANDA says.

[73] In the film, ADAM answers, "No!"

KIP: Well, I haven't got time anyway.

Amanda. I'm on your side, I guess you know that. Why, you got me so convinced I may even go out and become a woman. Good night all.

He goes.

ADAM: And he wouldn't have far to go, either.

AMANDA: Shhhh!

ADAM: What's the matter?

KIP *(coming back and speaking in a whisper)*: He can hear you!

[*He goes again. A moment passes. They return to dinner.*

ADAM *(in deep disgust)*: Like the World Series! Did you hear him?

AMANDA: Well, it is sort of a World Series. Isn't it?]

Dissolve to:

Insert—a Newspaper Article

[*Page three. The three-column headline reads:*

MORAL LAW UNFAIR TO FEMALE SEX SAYS MRS. BONNER

Continues Argument of Case against Husband.

The story follows. A candid shot of AMANDA, *her mouth open, accompanies the text.*][74]

Dissolve to:

Interior, the Courtroom—Full Shot

The spectators' benches are filled. The press table, crowded. On the stand, MISS BERYL CAIGHN. ADAM *has been questioning her. She is crying softly.*

ADAM: And then what happened?

BERYL: And then I heard a noise and—

ADAM: What sort of a noise?

BERYL *(explicitly)*: Like a sound. Like a loud sound. Going off.

---

[74] In the film, instead: A newspaper with large pictures of AMANDA and ADAM on the front page, small pictures of DORIS and ATTINGER. The headlines read:

> NEW YORK RECORD
> ATTINGER WITNESSES
> FACE FURTHER PROBE
> Box Score
> Wolves 7—Panthers 3
> She's 0—He's 0

ADAM: Yes?

BERYL: So I jumped up. And then all of a sudden I sawr her— *(She points to* MRS. ATTINGER*)*

ADAM: Mrs. Attinger?

BERYL: Yes.

ADAM: Say so, please.

BERYL: I seen Mrs. Attinger. And she was comin' after me with this gun of hers right in her two hands. So I think I must have started to conk out or—excuse me, to faint or somethin' and Mr. Attinger grabbed me so's I wouldn't fall down, I guess—so then she, Mrs. Attinger, tried to kill me.

[AMANDA *(on her feet, swiftly)*: Objection. I beg the Court to instruct the witness to refrain from rendering a decision.][75]

THE JUDGE: 'Stain 'at. Jury, dis'gar' 'ply.

[Medium Shot (Angle)—the Jury, *expressionless.*]

Medium Shot—the Room

THE JUDGE'S VOICE: Stri' fr'm rec'd. Wi'ness, plea' 'fine 'self to 'cital fac's.

ADAM: What did she do?

BERYL: She shot me. *At* me. I mean she tried to shoot me.

ADAM: How do you know that?

BERYL: Because she did it. So then he jumped in front of me, Warren—Mr. Attinger—and I ran in the hall hollering and then I fainted and then everything went black.

ADAM *(to* AMANDA*)*: Your witness.

AMANDA *(to* BERYL*)*: Everything went black a little earlier, didn't it?

BERYL *(confused)*: What?

AMANDA: I refer to the color of the silk negligee you put on to receive Mr. Attinger.

ADAM: Objection. Irrelevant.

AMANDA: Not at all.

---

[75] Instead, in the film:
AMANDA: Objection. Will the Court please instruct the witness to refrain from testifying to conclusions?

ADAM: What does it matter what color she was wearing?

AMANDA: A lot.

ADAM: Oh, come now—

THE JUDGE: 'Ruled.

ADAM: Exception.

AMANDA: *Were* you wearing a black silk lace negligee? *(See film still 13.)*

BERYL: Yes.

AMANDA: [What else?][76]

BERYL: What?

AMANDA *(angry)*: Answer the question!

BERYL: I can't remember.

AMANDA: Shoes? Slippers?

BERYL: Yes.

AMANDA: Which?

BERYL: Slippers.

AMANDA: Stockings?

BERYL: Yes . . .

AMANDA: Think again.

BERYL: No.

AMANDA: Nothing else?

BERYL: Yes.

AMANDA: What?

BERYL: A hair ribbon.

AMANDA: Is this your usual costume for receiving casual callers?

ADAM: 'Jection.

THE JUDGE: 'Stained.

AMANDA: 'Thdrawn. You say Mr. Attinger had come to see you about—?

BERYL: About another insurance policy. I said this already.

AMANDA: Well, say it again.

BERYL: Mr. Attinger came to collect on my policy and explain me another kind.

[76] In the film, instead:
AMANDA: Speak up, Miss Caighn. We're all very interested—
BERYL: Yes.
AMANDA: —in what you have to say. What else?

AMANDA: You hold—?

BERYL: Straight life. Three thousand.

AMANDA: And he came to discuss—?

BERYL: Health and accident.

AMANDA: He showed remarkable foresight in this, wouldn't you say?

ADAM: Will Your Honor instruct counsel to refrain from these sly and feminine hints to the jury?

AMANDA: I'll withdraw the question, Your Honor, on condition that the word "feminine" be stricken from the record.

ADAM: So be it.

THE JUDGE: So ordered.

[AMANDA: Now, Miss Caighn, a while ago I heard you say—*(She refers to a note)* "Mr. Attinger grabbed me."][77]

BERYL: Yes.

AMANDA: Had he ever grabbed you before?

BERYL: No.

AMANDA: Never before?

BERYL: No.

AMANDA: You are aware that you are still under oath, Miss Caighn, and that any false answer makes you liable to perjury?

BERYL: Yes.

AMANDA: Mr. Attinger had never touched you before this time?

BERYL: Sure . . . .

AMANDA: Ah?

BERYL: We used to shake hands quite a lot.

AMANDA: I see. Did you enjoy it?

ADAM: Objection!

THE JUDGE *(laughing)*: 'Stained.

[77] In the film, instead:
AMANDA: Miss Caighn—uh—a while ago, you said—uh—uh— Would you be kind enough to read me some of Miss Caighn's testimony? Uh— she'd just fainted, I believe—for the first time.
STENOGRAPHER: Uh—she had—"So I guess I must have started to conk out or something—excuse me, to faint or something, so Mr. Attinger grabbed me so—"
AMANDA: Ah, that's it. Thank you very much. You said Mr. Attinger grabbed you.

Dissolve to:

Insert—a Tabloid Newspaper

The headline reads:

ACCUSED LOVE-NESTER
ON STAND TODAY

Dissolve to:

Interior, the Courtroom—Full Shot

ATTINGER *is on the stand. He is in many bandages.* AMANDA *is working on him.*

AMANDA: And the year before *that* what did you buy your wife for her birthday.

ATTINGER: Nothing.

AMANDA: Nothing again! And the year before that?

ATTINGER: I don't remember.

AMANDA: You don't remember because there is nothing *to* remember.

ATTINGER: Wait a second—

AMANDA: Husbands remember the gifts they give, Mr. Attinger. *(See film still 14.)*

ATTINGER: Okay. So I didn't.

AMANDA: Why? Had she ceased to be a good wife to you?[78]

ATTINGER: No. She was okay.

AMANDA: Mr. Attinger—do you wish to see justice done in this case?

ATTINGER: Yes.

AMANDA: Very well, then. Tell the truth. Do you love your wife? Tell the truth.

ATTINGER: No.

AMANDA *(a step closer)*: Did you love her before she shot you? Tell the truth.

ATTINGER: When before?

AMANDA *(still closer; the effect is hypnotic)*: The day before?

---

[78] While these lines are being said, we see ADAM take off his glasses and stare at DORIS's hat, which is of course the hat he gave AMANDA. DORIS begins to cry.

ATTINGER: No.

AMANDA: When did you meet Beryl Caighn?

ATTINGER: A year. Maybe and a half.

AMANDA: And when did you stop loving your wife? Tell the truth.

ATTINGER: At least three years.

AMANDA: Why? Tell the truth.

ATTINGER *(under the spell)*: She started getting too fat.

AMANDA: Did you tell her that?

ATTINGER: Yes.

AMANDA: And what happened?

ATTINGER: She got fatter.

AMANDA: Did you ever strike her?

ATTINGER: Not much.

AMANDA: Yes or no.

ATTINGER: Yes.

AMANDA: Knock her down?

ATTINGER: What?

AMANDA: You heard me. Did you ever knock her down? Tell the truth!

ATTINGER: Maybe a couple times she tripped. Or slipped.

AMANDA: Scold her?

ATTINGER: Well—

AMANDA: Yes or no.

ATTINGER: Yes.

AMANDA: Stay out all night?

ATTINGER: Yes.

AMANDA: Do you consider yourself a good husband?

ATTINGER: Yes.

AMANDA: That's all.

> ADAM *gets up and moves to the witness.*
>
> *The jury, in the background, is static and still.*

ADAM: Did your wife ever scold you?

ATTINGER: Yes.

ADAM: Strike you?

ATTINGER: Yes.

ADAM: Knock you down?

ATTINGER: Yes.

ADAM: Stay out all night?

ATTINGER: No. I wish she did.

ADAM: Never mind the comment. Just answer the questions.

ATTINGER: What I'm doing. All day now.

ADAM: Now you listen carefully. Did your wife ever threaten you?

ATTINGER: Sure. Yes.

ADAM: When?

ATTINGER: Every day.

ADAM: And what effect did this have on you?

ATTINGER: It made me into a nervous wreck.

ADAM: How else did she mistreat you?

ATTINGER: In bed. She used to hit me in my sleep.

ADAM: How?

ATTINGER: What do you mean, how? With her fist.

ADAM: You're sure this was not your imagination?

ATTINGER: You don't get a split lip from imagination. She used to wait until I fell asleep then—pow! pow! So then an argument. So then I would go to sleep again. So then—pow! pow!

ADAM: And this caused you great distress?

ATTINGER: Yes. Also sleepless nights.

Dissolve to:

Insert—Newspaper

  The front page. A lurid layout. The head reads:
  [BERYL HOMEWRECKER,
  CHARGES DORIS][79]

---

[79] In the film, there are pictures of DORIS, ATTINGER, and BERYL. The headlines read:

NEW YORK GLOBE
City
Edition

r of Three Shot
y Infuriated Spouse

DORIS ATTINGER ON
STAND TO TELL ALL

Wife to Bare
Full Story
To Jury

66

Dissolve to:
Interior, the Courtroom—Full Shot
A demure MRS. ATTINGER *is on the stand.*

MRS. ATTINGER: So I says to him, listen Warren I says you can't have it both ways you know so make up your mind and don't you try and make some kind of part-timer out of me. Se he says bite your tongue, Fatso. So I says will you be home for supper so he says I'll write you a letter so I says will you be home later? So he says I'll put an ad in the New York Times personal column and let you know. So I said don't get too sassy Mr. Attinger. So he said and don't you be looking at me so cockeyed because I don't wanna hafta shake your head up to straighten them out. So I threw it.

AMANDA: Threw what?

MRS. ATTINGER: The pot. And so he left, mad.

AMANDA: And that was the last you saw him?

MRS. ATTINGER: Until later, when I followed him up and caught him muzzlin' that tall job.

ADAM: Objection.

THE JUDGE: 'Stained. 'Struct jury bear mind 'tivity not yet prove'.

AMANDA *(to* MRS. ATTINGER*)*: Now when you entered Apartment 2D. What did you see?

MRS. ATTINGER: Them clutching.

AMANDA: How close together were they [standing]?

MRS. ATTINGER: No close. Together.

AMANDA: No space between them?

MRS. ATTINGER: No space.

AMANDA: Where were her hands?

MRS. ATTINGER: On his ears.

AMANDA: On his ears?

MRS. ATTINGER: One on each ear. *(A sudden thought)* Maybe that's why he didn't hear me come in.

AMANDA: Where were his hands?

MRS. ATTINGER: Who knows?

AMANDA: You didn't see them?

MRS. ATTINGER: Around her someplace.

AMANDA: And were you surprised?

MRS. ATTINGER: No. I figured.

AMANDA: But it enraged you?

ADAM: Objection. Leading.

THE JUDGE: 'Stained.

AMANDA: What happened when you saw them thus embraced?

MRS. ATTINGER *(thinks hard for a moment)*: It enraged me.

AMANDA: Then what?

MRS. ATTINGER: I pressed the gun.

AMANDA: And— ?

MRS. ATTINGER *(with a shrug)*: Bang!

AMANDA: Did you take careful aim?

MRS. ATTINGER: I was too nervous.

AMANDA: Did you aim at all?

MRS. ATTINGER: I was too nervous.

AMANDA: Did you, at that moment, desire to kill Beryl Caighn?

MRS. ATTINGER: No.

AMANDA: To wound her?

MRS. ATTINGER: No.

AMANDA: To frighten her?

MRS. ATTINGER: Yes.

AMANDA: To kill your husband, Warren Attinger?

MRS. ATTINGER: No.

AMANDA: To wound him?

MRS. ATTINGER: No.

AMANDA: To frighten him?

MRS. ATTINGER: No.

AMANDA: No?

MRS. ATTINGER: No. [He's got a weak stomach. Who can afford it?]

AMANDA: In other words, you fired the pistol only to frighten Miss Caighn.

MRS. ATTINGER: Yes.

AMANDA: And what was the point of that?

MRS. ATTINGER: I got three children. She was breakin' up my home. *(She weeps)*

[Medium Shot—the Jury, *immobile.*
AMANDA's VOICE *(offscreen):* Thank you.]

Full Shot—the Room
> ADAM *takes over, as* AMANDA *sits down.*

ADAM: That's fine, Mrs. Attinger, you just go on and cry. But somewhere between sobs I wish you could find time to tell us just who it is you are crying for. Is it for Beryl Caighn, an innocent bystander to your sordid domestic failure? Or is it for your husband, driven ill by your shrewishness? Or for your children cursed with an unstable and irresponsible mother? Or for yourself?

AMANDA: I object to the pre-peroration, Your Honor, in its entirety as prejudicial to the defendant.

THE JUDGE: Oh, let it stand. I can't see that it much matters. 'V'ruled.

AMANDA: Exception.

THE JUDGE: But do get on with it, Mr. Bonner.

[ADAM: Your husband has told us, Mrs. Attinger, that you are subject to frequent fits of temper. What do you say to this?

> AMANDA *is on her feet.*

AMANDA: I must rise to object to this line, Your Honor.

ADAM: Now, wait—

> *The* BAILIFF *is rapping his gavel.*

AMANDA: This outrageous attempt to paint the defendant as a lunatic of some sort. Mrs. Attinger is a fine, healthy, a normal wife and mother and woman—

THE JUDGE: A moment—

AMANDA: But let me remind all here that in the words of the poet Congreve—

> "Heaven has no rage like love to hatred turned
> Nor Hell a fury like a woman scorned!"

> *(See film still 15.)*

THE JUDGE: Just a moment. *(To the* COURT REPORTER*)* Repeat the question.

Dissolve to:

Exterior, Bonner Apartment—from High—Long Shot

The sun is setting into the Towers of Babylon, known as the skyline, beyond.][80]

Interior, the Bonner Sitting Room—Full Shot

The room is as we have seen it before. This time we are close enough to a wall to see a large water color of "Bonner Hill." An incongruous piece of furniture has been added to the room. This is a folding massage table now spread for work. On the table, face down, his middle covered by a towel, is ADAM. *Beside the table, in the process of giving him an expert massage, is* AMANDA. *She wears pajama bottoms and a sweat-*

---

[80] Instead, in the film:

ADAM: Your husband has testified, Mrs. Attinger, that you have frequent fits of temper. What have you got—

AMANDA: I must rise to object—

ADAM: Oh, what are you going to do—object before I ask the question—?

AMANDA: —to this line, Your Honor. This outrageous attempt to paint the defendant as a kind of lunatic of some sort. Mrs. Attinger is a fine, healthy, a noble wife, mother—*(See film still 15.)*

The Judge removes his glasses and shouts, "Just a moment, please!"

AMANDA: May I remind the court of the words of the poet Congreve—

ADAM: The poet Congreve? Are you going to quote poetry—?

STENOGRAPHER: I can't take all this down, if you're both going—

AMANDA, *(over and above the others)*: "Heaven has no rage like love to hatred turned—"

ADAM *(ad libs)*: What are you doing? What are you doing—

AMANDA *(over and above* ADAM*)*: ". . . Nor Hell a fury like a woman scorned!"

JUDGE REISER shouts above them, tapping his glasses on the desk, "Now, just a moment! Read the question."

STENOGRAPHER: "Your husband has testified, Mrs. Attinger, that you are subject to frequent fits of violent temper. Now, what about—?"

Camera dissolves to a title card that reads, THAT EVENING.

shirt. Beside her, an end table has been moved into convenient position. It holds cold cream, alcohol, and almond oil. During the activity, ADAM *and* AMANDA *carry on a fitful conversation, between gasps and grunts.*[81]

ADAM: Hmmph!—but don't try to tell me—ho!—he's impartial because—ow!—every time I look—ooh—up at him, I can see him just—ho!

AMANDA: Quiet, please. It doesn't really—pah!—do you good if you don't—wait a second—relax.

ADAM: I'm relaxed.

AMANDA: You're not. I can feel.

ADAM: So—can I.

AMANDA: You can?

She hits him a whacking smack.

[Hey!][82]

AMANDA: Testing. *(She massages the back of his neck)*

ADAM: Oh, thank you, thank you. I seem to need this more and more every day.

AMANDA: You're aging fast, that's all.

ADAM: You can say that again.

AMANDA: All right, I will. You're aging fast, that's all.

ADAM: You're helping.

AMANDA: [All right,] done.

ADAM: Thanks.

As he gets off the table, the CAMERA *swings over toward* AMANDA, *who dashes some alcohol into her hands and rubs them together. Now she dries them and begins to remove her sweatshirt. As she does so, she walks out of the* SHOT *and* ADAM, *tying the sash of his robe, comes into her vacated position. He turns the sheet on the rubbing table.*

ADAM: Ought to be some news on. Want it?

[81] In the film, this scene takes place in the bedroom, and AMANDA is wearing a towel.
[82] In the film, instead:
ADAM: Um—oow! What are you doing?

71

AMANDA'S VOICE: If it's good news, yes.

ADAM: Try my best.

He goes to the radio, the CAMERA FOLLOWING—*and turns it on. He presses a button.*

AMANDA: Why don't they have all the good news on one station and all the bad news on another station, now why wouldn't that be good?

[ADAM: Lie down.][83]

He moves toward her, CAMERA FOLLOWING. *The radio, warmed up now, sings out. The voice of one of the most popular singers in the land is singing his heart out, with volume and vitality. The song is "Farewell, Amanda."* ADAM *dives back to the radio and shuts it off.* AMANDA'S *gentle laugh is heard, off.*

ADAM: [I guess] I got the station with the *bad* news.

He goes to the table. AMANDA *lies there, face down, the towel across her. The* CAMERA MOVES IN TO:

Close Two-Shot—Amanda and Adam

ADAM *starts to give her her rubdown.*

AMANDA: Getting awfully popular, Kip's song. I hear it everywhere.

ADAM: Me, too. I even hear it when it isn't playing.

AMANDA *(softly singing)*: "Farewell, Amanda, Adios, addio, adieu—"

ADAM *moves out of the* SHOT. AMANDA *continues with a rather dreamy rendition of her song. Suddenly, from offscreen, we hear the sound of a solid flesh-on-flesh smack!* AMANDA *wheels over as the* CAMERA RIDES IN TO:

[Extreme Close-up—Amanda's Outraged Face

AMANDA *(a shriek)*: Pinky!] *(See film still 16.)*

Medium Shot—Adam

He is getting some cold cream out of a jar preparatory to acting as AMANDA'S *masseur. He looks over at her, innocence*

---

[83] In the film, instead:

ADAM: Um. I guess nobody—ever thought of that—

personified. (Throughout this scene ADAM *tries to hold on to the two globs of cold cream in either hand. The difficulty of this is increased when he makes a forceful fist and the cold cream squooshes through his fingers.)*

Medium Shot—Amanda
She is off the table, pulling on her sweatshirt, her back to ADAM *and the* CAMERA. *She looks over her shoulder at him, eyes flashing.* ADAM *comes to her, moving into the* SHOT.
ADAM: Something the matter? *(A little pause)* Don't you want your rub? *(Another pause)* What's the beef? You sore about a little slap?
AMANDA: No.
ADAM: Then what?
AMANDA *(her eyes narrowing)*: You meant that, didn't you? You really meant it!
ADAM: No, I—
AMANDA: You did. I can tell. I know your touch. I can tell a slap from a slug.
ADAM: Okay, okay.
AMANDA: I'm not so sure it is. I'm not so sure I want to be subjected to typical—to instinctive—masculine—brutality.
ADAM *(calming her)*: Oh, now look.
He nearly drops some cold cream on the floor.
AMANDA *(rubbing her hip)*: And it felt not only as though you meant it but also as though you thought you had a right to. I can tell.
ADAM: What have you got back there? Radar equipment?
AMANDA: You're really sore at me, aren't you?
ADAM *(with a measured beat)*: Don't be diriculous. Ridiculous.
AMANDA *(pointing finger)*: There! Proves it.
ADAM: [All right then, I am. What about it?
AMANDA: Why are you?
ADAM: You know why.
AMANDA: Kip? Just because he's having fun?
ADAM: No. You. You having fun and in the wrong way. Down at

the trial. You're shaking the tail of the law, Amanda—trying to—and I don't like it. I'm ashamed of you.

His words suddenly wound her. Tears well up in her eyes and her throat catches.

AMANDA: You don't say.

ADAM: We've disagreed on plenty—that's okay. I try to see your point always, but I'm stumped now, baby.

AMANDA: You don't even try to see why I—if you respected my—

She can't go on. She's in tears.

ADAM: Oh, fine! Here we go. The old juice. Never fails, does it? Guaranteed heart-melter. A few female tears. Stronger than the strongest acid. Well, not this time. You can cry from now until the jury comes back in—it won't make you right and it won't win your silly case.

AMANDA *(appealing)*: Adam, please. Please understand.

ADAM: Nothing doing.

A pause. She sits down on the sofa and weeps. ADAM *watches her for a moment, then speaks. Her tears succeed, as usual.*

ADAM *(softly)*: You want your rubdown? (AMANDA *shakes her head. He comes a step closer)* You want a drink? *(She shakes her head again. He moves forward another step)* You want anything? *(She nods.* ADAM *comes closer still)* What?

She kicks him in the shin. He springs back with a cry.

AMANDA *(quietly and in perfect control)*: That. *(She rises)* Let's *all* be manly!][84]

---

[84] In the film, instead:

ADAM: All right, all right, I am . . . sore. I am sore. What about it?

AMANDA: Why are you?

ADAM: You know why.

AMANDA: You mean Kip? Just because he's having a little fun?

ADAM: No. Because you're having a little fun. You're having the wrong kind of fun—down in that courtroom. You're shaking the law by the tail, and I don't like it. I'm ashamed of you, Amanda.

AMANDA: Is that so?

ADAM: Yes, that's so. We've had our little differences and I've always tried to see your point of view, but this time you've got me stumped, baby.

AMANDA: You haven't tried to see my point to view. You haven't even any respect for my, my, my—

ADAM: There we go, there we go, there we go— Oh, oh, here we go again.

Dissolve to:

Insert—a **Newspaper Article,** *illustrated with a cartoon of a Punch and Judy stage. The figures are caricatures of* ADAM *and* AMANDA. *The caption reads:*

GOTHAM TODAY

Interior, the Courtroom—Full Shot

It is crowded and tense. ADAM *and* AMANDA *are both on their feet.*

ADAM: And represents a wanton waste of the taxpayers' money.

AMANDA *(ever so softly)*: I have called these few witnesses to assist me in graphically illustrating my point that woman, as the equal of man, is entitled to equality before the law.

ADAM *looks off.*

Medium Shot—What He Sees

On the witnesses' bench, a row of fourteen women. All kinds. Old, young, well-dressed, and shabby. And one with a beard.[85]

ADAM'S VOICE: We'll be here for a year.

The old juice— Ah, guaranteed heart-melter. A few female tears—
AMANDA *(sobbing)*: I can't help it—
ADAM: —stronger than any acid. But this time they won't work—
AMANDA: I didn't—
ADAM: You can cry from now until the time the jury comes in and it won't make you right and it won't win you that silly case.
AMANDA *(sobbing)*: Adam! Please, please try to undersst-t-. . . .
ADAM: Nothing doing—
AMANDA *(offscreen)*: . . . t-tand.
ADAM: Ah, don't you want your rubdown? You want a drink?
AMANDA: No.
ADAM: Do you want anything? What, honey? (*She kicks him in the shin*)
ADAM: Ow!
AMANDA: Let's all be manly!
[85] The following dialogue is heard offscreen:
AMANDA: They have been carefully selected to testify in this case. Each representing a particular branch of American womanhood. For not only one woman is on trial here, but all women.
ADAM: Your Honor, I submit that not one of this long string of witnesses has any direct bearing on the case.
AMANDA: For years, women have been ridiculed, pampered, chucked under the chin. I ask you, on behalf of us all, be fair to the fair sex.

75

Medium Shot—Up Front

The JUDGE, AMANDA, ADAM, *and staffs.*

THE JUDGE: Mrs. Bonner, couldn't you cover the ground with, say, three witnesses?

[AMANDA: Oh, well. Call Doctor Margaret Brodeigh!][86]

AMANDA, *in a pet, flings down her pencil. It rolls over to* ADAM. *He throws his down—in her direction.*

[THE CLERK: Dr. Margaret Brodeigh.]

Medium Shot—under the Table, *as* AMANDA *and* ADAM *bend to get their pencils. The* SHOT *favors* ADAM*, who curls his lip at the upside-down* AMANDA.[87]

[Wild Lines for Amanda—to Cut Into Scene 118[88]—as Adam Looks off at the Witness Bench—and Camera Pans along the Witnesses:

AMANDA: Look at them! A simple, representative group—important to our cause, Your Honor, Ladies and Gentlemen, since not only one woman is on trial here, but all women. Through years of injustice, patronized, ridiculed, pampered, tolerated, chucked under the chin—discriminated against. I ask you on behalf of us all—*(pleading tone)* be fair to the Fair Sex!] *See footnote*[85]

Medium Shot—the Reverse—Favoring Amanda

She sticks her tongue out.

Meanwhile, DR. MARGARET BRODEIGH *approaches the stand.*

Again we hear the CLERK's *voice:*

CLERK *(offscreen):* Place your left hand on the Bible and raise your

[86] In the film:
AMANDA: Well, uh, Dr. Margaret Brodeigh, would you take the stand, please?
[87] While this is going on, the following dialogue is heard:
CLERK: With this witness to be examined, this case will certainly continue for at least two or three days. With Your Honor's permission, I'll report that no new cases are to be added to our day calendar.
JUDGE REISER: So ordered.
[88] That is, the following scene.

right hand. You do solemnly swear that the evidence you shall give to the Court and Jury in this case shall be the truth, the whole truth and nothing but the truth, so help you God?

DR. BRODEIGH's VOICE *(offscreen)*: I do.

CLERK: Please be seated and state your name and address.

DR. BRODEIGH's VOICE *(offscreen)*: Doctor Margaret Brodeigh. Fifty-eight East Eighty-eighth Street.

Full Shot—the Room, *as* ADAM *and* AMANDA *return to the top of the room.* AMANDA *moves to the stand.* DR. BRODEIGH *is an exceedingly handsome young woman.*

AMANDA: Dr. Brodeigh, will you be good enough to state your age?

DR. BRODEIGH: Thirty-three.

AMANDA: Your occupation?

DR. BRODEIGH: Chemist.

AMANDA: Will you please state what position or positions you now hold?

DR. BRODEIGH: Gladly. Chief Consulting Chemist, Institute for Advanced Studies; Director, Brodeigh-Halleck Laboratories;

[**Close Shot—the Judge**

He removes his glasses and takes a closer look at the witness.][89]

DR. BRODEIGH's VOICE *(continuing)*: Civilian Consultant, United States Army Chemical Warfare Service;

Close Shot—Amanda, *delighted.*

DR. BRODEIGH's VOICE *(without pause)*: Advisor to Supply Officer, British Embassy;

Medium Shot—the Jury

Still no expression.

DR. BRODEIGH's VOICE: Director of Chemical Field Research, United States Department of Agriculture.

[89] In the film it is ADAM who removes his glasses.

Full Shot—the Room

DR. BRODEIGH: That's *this* year.

AMANDA: Will you please state what degrees you hold?

DR. BRODEIGH: Well, let's see. A.B., B.S.—Bryn Mawr. M.A., Ph.D., M.D.—Columbia— Then—do you want the European ones, too?

THE JUDGE *(fascinated)*: Please.

Close-up—Adam, *bored and a little angry.*[90]

Dissolve to:

Medium Shot—the Stand

It is now occupied by a hearty woman in a leather Air Force jacket.

AMANDA: I see. And how many months have you been foreman, Mrs. McGrath?

MRS. MCGRATH: Seventeen.

AMANDA: And this promotion placed under you how many?

MRS. MCGRATH: Three-eight-three.

AMANDA: Any men?

MRS. MCGRATH: Mostly.

AMANDA: They didn't complain?

MRS. MCGRATH: Couldn't. Seniority.

AMANDA: Does your husband object to your employment?

MRS. MCGRATH: No.

AMANDA: Is he employed?

MRS. MCGRATH: Yes.

AMANDA: Where?

MRS. MCGRATH *(a grin)*: Under me.

Close-up—Adam, Closer than Before

He looks a little ill.

---

[90] In the film, DR. BRODEIGH is heard saying, ". . . Diplôme des Sciences Chimiques de la Sorbonne, Paris, Docteur 'Honora-Scholar' de Philosophie, Université . . ."

Dissolve to:

Medium Shot—Still Another Angle

> *This one has* ADAM *in the background. On the stand, a chunky woman of unguessable age. She is hatless and wears an old trench coat.*

AMANDA: Now just what do you mean by "show business," Miss LaPere?

MISS LAPERE: I mean all different kinds of show business. Carnival, vaudeville, Ringling Brothers, night clubs. Even legit once.

AMANDA: And just what is it that you do? *(See film still 17.)*

MISS LAPERE: It changes, see. Like take for instance, tumbling. I used to do quite a lot of that, tumbling. Then it gets corny and I'm stuck with [a double backward somersault from the ground and]—[91]

AMANDA: Just what is that?

MISS LAPERE: Well, it's a—you start from—well, look—*(She hops down, kicks a chair out of the way and does one.[92] Then she returns to the witness stand)* That's it. But nobody wants it, see? Corny. So then I done some trapeze work and high bar. But now I'm a little heavy for that, so two years back, I got into this lift act. I'm one of the only female *under*standers around.

AMANDA: Yes.

MISS LAPERE: We do this open pyramid where I support five men.

AMANDA: Surely you're not the only female who does that?

MISS LAPERE: No, I mean in the act, see—oh, a gag. Hey, that's pretty good—*(She laughs)* Yeah, support—[no, see I meant—I get this Greek hold and then they lift] say, that was a good one.

THE JUDGE: 'S get on, coun' shall we?

AMANDA: What do you consider your best physical or athletic accomplishment?

MISS LAPERE: My lifts, I guess. I was out last year. These three Olympic guys and me. Just lifts. I done the finish where I lifted the champ with his barbell together.

---

[91] In the film, she says "a roll of flip-flap, and I—"

[92] In the film OLYMPIA turns somersaults across the room.

AMANDA: What?

MISS LAPERE: Yeah. It was a good act. See, they lift—lift—lift. Then the last guy, he done a one-hand three-hundred-and-fifty barbell lift. Then while he still had it up I come on and lift him up with his barbell together. Peeled down, see, so they could tell I was a woman.

AMANDA: Remarkable.

MISS LAPERE: Yeah, we used to get a good hand.

AMANDA: Can you lift any man?

MISS LAPERE *(modestly)*: Well, I don't know.

AMANDA: Do you think you could lift Mr. Bonner?

MISS LAPERE: Who's he?

ADAM *(springing up)*: Your Honor—I protest against this farce.

AMANDA: That's him.

MISS LAPERE *(appraisingly)*: Oh, sure.

[AMANDA *(quietly)*: Go ahead. *(*MISS LAPERE *slips off her coat and advances on* ADAM)

ADAM *(concentrated on the* JUDGE*)*: May it please the Court, I wish to object most strongly to the tactics being used in this matter for no other reason than—

At this point, he is seized from behind. MISS LAPERE *grabs him. One hand on the nape of his neck—the other on his inner thigh—a single grunt from* MISS LAPERE *and* ADAM *finds himself high off the ground—eye-level with the* JUDGE. MISS LAPERE *walks around now with the stiff and terrified* ADAM *aloft.*

ADAM: Your Honor.

AMANDA *(to the* JURY*)*: Ladies and Gentlemen, I have attempted to demonstrate, with the few witnesses allotted me, that woman can be quite the equal of man in any and all fields—*if* given the opportunity. I have shown you scientific, artistic, industrial, and raw physical examples of achievement.

ADAM *(from high)*: May it please the Court. *(See film still 18.)*

AMANDA: Let your imaginations, then, consider the possibilities of equality in other matters. Marital and moral, to be specific.

ADAM: Put me down.

AMANDA *(to* MISS LAPERE*)*: Put him down.

THE JUDGE: Yes. Put him down. *(See film still 19.)*

MISS LAPERE *(looking up)*: Relax!

She starts to bend her knees and put him upright. ADAM
slips away and falls.

MISS LAPERE: You didn't relax.

ADAM *gets up slowly, ready for murder.*][93]

Dissolve to:

[Exterior, Bonner Apartment—Medium Shot

*The entry. A party of six, dressed to the nines, wait for a
taxi. The doorman is trying to whistle one up.*][94]

[93] In the film, ADAM is heard saying, "I call the Counsel's attention that she
is guilty of a grave offense against the profession."

ADAM walks around his table and continues, "May it please the court,
I strenuously object to the methods being used in this matter, Your Honor,
for no other reason than its an—" AMANDA says quietly to OLYMPIA
LAPERE, "Go ahead." ADAM continues, "It's an insult to the dignity of the
Court."

OLYMPIA *(to* AMANDA*)*: All right, I will.

ADAM: Now, we all love the circus. I love it just as much as anybody else,
I'm sure. But it seems to me—(OLYMPIA *bends down and starts to pick up*
ADAM) No, no, no, no, no, no—(OLYMPIA *picks him up*) No, no, no, no,
no, no, no, no, no, no, no."

OLYMPIA: And I'll get you up here like this, see, like this. (*She holds him
over her head while the crowd laughs. The* JUDGE *bangs his gavel and says,
"Put him down!"* EMERALD *and* KIP *are seen laughing in the crowd*)

AMANDA: Your Honor, I am only attempting to show you with the few . . .

ADAM: Get me down.

OLYMPIA: You're all right, honey. All right.

ADAM: Get me down.

AMANDA: ". . . witnesses allotted—"

THE JUDGE: Come on down from there.

ADAM: Your Honor—Your—

JUDGE REISER bangs his hand on the bench and says, "Put him down!"

AMANDA *(to* OLYMPIA*)*: Put him down. Put him down.

ADAM: Let me down.

OLYMPIA puts him down and says, "There you are. Now, it wasn't as
bad as you thought it was."

AMANDA: Consider then the possibility—

[94] In the film, a title card reads:

THAT EVENING

Interior, the Bonner Home—Full Shot

[*The sitting room. This time* ADAM *is the one sitting beside the tray of drinks, waiting. He is reading a newspaper. At the same time, the voice of a newscaster emanates from the radio. Now the newscast ends, and simultaneously,* ADAM *drops the newspaper on the floor. He moves to the radio and shuts it off. He returns to the tray and mixes himself a fresh drink.* AMANDA *comes into the hall, high and happy.*

AMANDA *(calling out)*: Darling? *(She moves into the room)* Gosh, I'm sorry to be late but—

ADAM *picks up his drink and walks out of the room.* AMANDA *is stunned. This has never happened before. Never. Her voice is pure dismay.*

AMANDA: Adam!][95]

Off, a door slams. AMANDA *moves out after him slowly.*

Medium Shot—Interior, the Kitchen

ADAM *cuts a slice of bread.* AMANDA *comes in.*

AMANDA: Darling please.

ADAM *puts the bread back into the bread box. Puts the knife away. Carries the slice of bread to the refrigerator and looks for something to go with it.*

AMANDA: You real mad? Or is this a tease? Or what? *(He finds some cheese)* Real mad. *(No answer. There is just a touch of panic in her voice as she goes on)* Shouldn't we talk about it? Don't you want to hear *my* side?

ADAM *takes his bread, cheese, and walks out of the kitchen.*

[AMANDA, *left alone, turns on the water tap. She lets it run at*

----

[95] AMANDA enters the apartment, puts her purse on a chair, and walks toward ADAM, who is sitting on the sitting-room sofa with a drink. She hides a gift behind her back, saying, "Hello, thing. I'm sorry I'm so late, darling, but I—"

AMANDA sits down on the sofa next to him and puts her feet up on the coffee table. ADAM sips his drink and doesn't look up. AMANDA starts to pour herself a drink, but the tumbler is empty, to her dismay. She holds out the gift, saying, "Guess who this is for? ADAM." ADAM glances at her, gets up, and leaves the room without a word.

full pressure, gets a glass, goes to the sink and drinks three glasses of water in quick succession. Now she goes out.][96]

Full Shot—Interior, the Bedroom, *across* ADAM, *who lies on his back, his hands under his head, his eyes wide open. He is on the double bed.* AMANDA *comes in. He moves to the single bed.*
AMANDA: Don't you want to talk to me? *(*ADAM *turns away)* What is it? Did I go too far? If you think so then I'm sorry. Can't I apologize? Didn't *you* ever go too far?
ADAM *looks at her for a long moment.*
ADAM: Once.
He gets up and goes out to his dressing room. AMANDA *follows. The* CAMERA, *too.*

Medium Shot—Interior, Adam's Dressing Room
ADAM, *carrying his drink comes in, closes the door behind him. Sits down. The door opens.*
AMANDA *comes in. He rises, goes out to his bathroom.*

Medium Shot—Interior, Adam's Bathroom
ADAM *comes in, closes the door behind him. Sits on a bath stool. The door opens.* AMANDA *comes in and shuts the door behind her.*
AMANDA: [Now—listen.] Now—Adam, if I'm in the wrong I want to make it right but it seems to me, Adam, you're making a mountain out of something not even an ant hill—let alone a mole-hill—a hill of beans—not even . . .
ADAM: Excuse me.
AMANDA: Yes?
ADAM: May I say something?
AMANDA: Of course.
ADAM: Save your eloquence for the jury.
He starts out.
AMANDA: Adam, wait—

[96] In the film, AMANDA calls after him, "Adam!" She puts the gift down and starts removing her gloves.

Interior, the Dressing Room—Medium Shot

ADAM *comes in from the bathroom.* AMANDA *is in the doorway. She watches, horrified, as he begins to pack a bag. He continues to do so throughout the scene.*

AMANDA: Please forgive me.

ADAM: For what?

AMANDA: For whatever it is that's upset you.

ADAM: Oh, you don't know what it is?

AMANDA: Not exactly, no.

ADAM: That's just my point.

AMANDA: What point?

ADAM: We've been close—but never this close. This close I see something in you I never saw before and I don't like it. In fact, I hate it.

AMANDA: Go ahead.

ADAM: [Don't worry, I will.] *(He slams an article in)* Contempt for the law—that's what you've got—its a disease—a spreading— No respect—you think law is something to get around or get under or get over or just plain flout. Start with that and you wind up in the— Well, look at us! The law is the law—good or bad. *(He punctuates his tirade with his packing)* If it's bad the way to do is change it, not bust it apart. One law—pretty soon it's all law— then it's everything—*me.* You don't respect me, do you?

AMANDA: Not at the moment, no.

ADAM: Answer me this. What's marriage? What is it?

AMANDA: You tell *me.*

ADAM: All right—it's a contract—it's a law! Are you going to outsmart it like you do other laws? Clever—so clever. You've outsmarted me—outsmarted yourself—us—everything. You just get yourself focused on some dim-witted cause and you crash on regardless. You don't care what happens to me or to you—or what we seem like to people watching. Well, I'll tell you. Like two uncivilized nuts! Uncivilized! Just what sort of a blow you've struck or think you've struck for women's rights or whatever, I don't know—but you've certainly fouled *us* up beyond all recognition.

84

You've torn it right down the middle.

AMANDA: How?[97] Just how?

ADAM: I've done it all the way I said I would. Richer, poorer. Sickness, health. Better, worse—but this is *too* worse. This is basic! I'm old-fashioned! I like two sexes! Another thing. All of a sudden I don't like being married to what's known as the *new* woman. [I can't handle it. I don't know how.] I want a wife—not a competitor! *Competitor! Competitor!* If you want to be a big he-woman go ahead and be it—but not with me!!

[*He snaps his bag and stalks out.*

Interior, the Bedroom—Medium Shot

Panning, as ADAM *comes through carrying his bag, followed by* AMANDA.][98]

AMANDA: You're not going to solve anything running away. Where you going?

Interior, the Parlor—Full Shot

ADAM *comes bounding down the stairs,* AMANDA *near on his heels.*

AMANDA: Why don't you stand still and have it out? Where you going?

ADAM: Because I don't want to!

He has reached the hallway now, picked up his hat. AMANDA *runs around in front of him and grasps his lapels.*

AMANDA: Adam, please. I've said all the wrong things. I don't know what's the matter with me. You, too. You've said the wrong—

ADAM: Not me. I said what I meant.

[AMANDA *(violently)*: All right!!] *(See film still 20.)*

She swings him around and gives him a rough push toward

---

[97] ADAM takes his packed suitcase into the living room and goes to the desk, taking papers out of the drawers and putting them into his briefcase. AMANDA follows him.

[98] ADAM goes down the hallway, AMANDA running after him.

85

the door. ADAM, *off balance, falls against it, hard. He opens it, gets a good grip on the handle.*

AMANDA: Adam!

ADAM: What?

AMANDA: Don't you *dare* slam that door.

ADAM *(quietly)*: All right.

He leaves and slams the door with terrifying force.

Close Shot

The mirror beside AMANDA *falls with a crash. She jumps away to avoid it and knocks over a tall lamp. The* CAMERA FOLLOWS *to pick up the lamp as it hits a tall vase of gladioli—which falls, the* CAMERA FOLLOWING—*and hits the top of the automatic phonograph. It suddenly sings out:*

"Farewell, Amanda,
Adios, addio, adieu—"
and so on.

Close-up—Amanda

[*It's too much. She bursts into floods of tears.*][99]

Insert:

Another newspaper piece. This one is principally a photograph of ADAM *being held aloft by* MISS LAPERE. *The caption:*

ASS'T D.A. RISES
TO NEW HEIGHTS

Dissolve to:

Interior, the Courtroom—Full Shot

The crowded room. Up and down the sides of the room, rows of people standing. The press table is busy. AMANDA, *on her feet, has reached the climax of her peroration.*

AMANDA *(to the* JURORS*)*: —and so the question here is equality

---

[99] In the film AMANDA, in a fury, slams the door several times and exits up the stairs.

before the law—regardless of religion, color, wealth—or as in this instance—sex. Excuse me. *(See film still 21.)*
She removes her jacket and takes a sip of water. Now, in blouse and skirt, she returns to the fray.
AMANDA: Law, like man, is composed of two parts. Just as a man is body and soul, so is the law letter and spirit. The law says, "Thou shalt not kill!" Yet men *have* killed and proved a reason and been set free. Self-defense—defense of others, of wife or children or home. If a thief breaks into your home and you shoot him, the law will not deal harshly with you. Nor, indeed, should it. Thus, you are asked here to judge not whether or not these acts were committed, but to what extent they were justified.

Now, Ladies and Gentlemen of the Jury, I respectfully request that you join me in a revealing experiment.

Medium Shot—the Jury, *attentive.*
AMANDA'S VOICE: I ask you all to direct your attention to the defendant, Mrs. Attinger.
Twelve heads turn, as though propelled by a lever, as though watching a tennis match.

Close Shot—Mrs. Attinger
With all eyes upon her, she is suddenly shy.

Close Shot—Amanda
AMANDA: Now, keep looking at her. Keep watching.

Medium Shot—the Jury, *working at the instruction.*
AMANDA'S VOICE: Listen carefully. Look at her. Look at her hard.

Close Shot—Mrs. Attinger
AMANDA'S VOICE *(hypnotically)*: Now imagine her a man. Go on, now. Use your imaginations.

Medium Shot—the Jury
AMANDA'S VOICE: Think of her as a man sitting there.

87

Close Shot—Mrs. Attinger, *rather embarrassed by all this.*
AMANDA'S VOICE: Think of her as a man sitting there, accused of a like crime. [Think!]

> *And, of course, in some unaccountable way,* MRS. ATTINGER *becomes a man. He has her face and physical position, but he is a man, nevertheless. A man named* MRS. ATTINGER.

Medium Shot—the Jury, *transfixed.*

Close Shot—Mrs. Attinger
[AMANDA'S VOICE: All right, that's enough.

> *With the suddenness of a snap! the image returns to normal.*

Full Shot—the Room
AMANDA: Now, continuing. I ask you to hold that impression.

Medium Shot—the Jury
AMANDA'S VOICE: And look at *Mr.* Attinger.

> *Again the heads switch in unison.*

Close Shot—Mr. Attinger
AMANDA'S VOICE: And suppose him a woman.

Medium Shot—the Jury

> *They are finding this a bit harder to do. But they try.*

Close Shot—Mr. Attinger
AMANDA'S VOICE: Try. Try hard.

> MR. ATTINGER *changes into a woman, dressed as* MRS. ATTINGER *is dressed now, including the hat* ADAM *bought.*

AMANDA'S VOICE: All right, thank you.

> *He is back to normal in one frame.*

Medium Shot—Amanda and the Jury
AMANDA: And now, Miss Caighn.

> *The* JURY'S *heads turn once more.*

Close Shot—Beryl Caighn

AMANDA's VOICE: She's the third party. She's that slick home-wrecker. Picture her so.

A nervous BERYL is being slowly transformed into a standard smoothie, in a pin-stripe suit.

AMANDA's VOICE: A wolf. You know the type.

Suddenly, a mustache appears on BERYL's upper lip!

AMANDA's VOICE: All right.

BERYL *is back to normal.*][100]

Full Shot—the Room

The JURY, to say nothing of the subjects involved, have been somewhat shaken by the experiment.

AMANDA: Now you have it. Judge it so. An unwritten law stands back of a man who fights to defend his home. Apply the same to this maltreated wife and neglected mother. We ask you no more. Equality! *(Another sip of water)* Deep in the interior of South America, there thrives today a civilization, far older than ours, a people known as the Lorcananos, descended from the Amazons. In this vast tribe, members of the female sex rule and govern and systematically deny equal rights to the men—made weak and puny by years of subservience. Too weak to revolt. [We look upon this condition as a fantasy, a comic opera,] and yet, how long have we lived in the shadow of a like injustice?

Close Shot—Adam

He is looking at AMANDA with some awe, but more suspicion.

Medium Shot—the Bench—Amanda—and the Front of the Room

AMANDA:[I ask for a verdict of not guilty. There was never any

---

[100] AMANDA's voice is heard: "A husband who was only trying to protect his home. Now, hold it. Hold that impression and look at Beryl Caighn." The camera moves to BERYL. "Look at her. Look at her hard. A man, a slick home-wrecker, a third party—a wolf. You know the type." Beryl turns into a man with short dark hair and a mustache, wearing a man's suit. "All right, hold that impression and look at Mr. Attinger and suppose him a woman. Try. Try hard." ATTINGER turns into a woman with blond hair, wearing a woman's dress and a flowered hat. "Ah, yes, there she is, the guilty wife. Look at her. Does she arouse your sympathy?"

intent to kill. It was only an act of a woman to save her home. She merely meant to scare. She had no experience with firearms.] Consider this unfortunate woman's act as though you yourselves had each committed it. Every living being is capable of attack if sufficiently provoked. Assault lies dormant within us all. It waits only circumstance to set it in violent motion. [You have been a model jury—and I know that, unswayed by the vengeful tirade you will hear from the prosecutor— *(At this point, the* DISSOLVE *begins and an ectoplasmic* ADAM *appears)* you will remain a model jury and bring in a just verdict. Having done so, you will have earned not only the repose of the just, but the knowledge that you have contributed in no small way to—][101]

[*Here a long* DISSOLVE. *(Twenty feet?)*

AMANDA, *screen left.* ADAM, *screen right.* SOUND *and* PICTURE DISSOLVE *together, so that for about ten feet they are talking together, facing one another in effect, if not in time.*]

Interior, the Courtroom—Full Shot

ADAM *is on his feet and before the bench.*

ADAM: [—for your patience in the unusually trying circumstances surrounding this case. I apologize for any irritation I may have caused; for any lack of clarity in my presentation. *(The* DISSOLVE *is complete at this point)* This latter point I will attempt to rectify in the review which follows.] Let me say at the outset that the arguments advanced by the attorney for the defense were sound. *Mere* sound! *(He waits a beat for his laugh, none is forthcoming, so he plunges on)* Ladies and Joontlemen of the Jerry. That is to say, *Gentlemen* of the *Jury.* Much as I have enjoyed some portions of the entertainment which she has provided—I am bound to remind you that none of it had any real bearing on the case. Of course, I am going to ask you for a verdict of guilty as charged. You, not I, speak for the people—and the people wish you to say —citizens, abide by the law! No one can live in a community, and

[101] Instead, in the film, AMANDA adds, "I ask you for a verdict of not guilty. There was no murder attempt here—only a pathetic attempt to save a home."

feel safe, knowing that irresponsible and reckless neurotics are wandering about its thoroughfares armed with deadly weapons. You are expected to deal with criminals—

AMANDA *(springing to her feet)*: Objection!

ADAM: —as though you were—

AMANDA: Not brought out by testimony—exceeds fair bounds of summation.

ADAM: You are expected—

AMANDA: Wait for the ruling!

ADAM: Sit down, Pinkie! I didn't interrupt when—

THE JUDGE: Just a moment!

THE COURT REPORTER: I didn't get his last. *(He peers at his notes on the stenotype machine)* You said, 'Sit down, something."

ADAM *(embarrassed)*: No matter.

THE COURT REPORTER: May I have it for the record, please?

ADAM *(repeating it, softly)*: "Sit down, Pinkie."

THE COURT REPORTER: Pinkie?

ADAM: Yes.

THE COURT REPORTER: What's that, a name?

ADAM: Yes.

THE COURT REPORTER: Whose?

ADAM: The Attorney for the Defense.

THE COURT REPORTER: Oh! Is that y or i-e?

AMANDA: Y for him. I-e for me.

ADAM: Oh, let's get on, for the love of— What was your objection, Pinkie? *(He whips his pencil down, furious at his caught tongue)* Counsel!

AMANDA: I object to the characterization of the defendant as a criminal.

THE JUDGE: 'Stained. Jur' dis'gar' ref'ce.

AMANDA: A strange appellation, indeed, for one who—

THE JUDGE: All right.

AMANDA: Has an unblemished record—

THE JUDGE: I have ruled.

AMANDA: —as a citizen, wife, and mother—

ADAM: The Court has ruled!

AMANDA: All right *(then, very quietly),* Pinky.

She sits. ADAM *is good and rattled now. (See film still 22.)*

[ADAM: The purpose of a summation, as I have said, or rather as I meant to say, *is,* as I understand it, no more or less than—if in a Lourt of Caw, Court of Law— *(He is hopelessly muddled and bogged down now)* Excuse me, ladies and gentlemen. *(He takes a drink, glares at* AMANDA, *who smiles back her sweetest smile)* Let me begin again. As a jury, you are a most fortunate body. Your decision here is simple and clear. You need only decide whether she fired her husband at the, pistol at her husband, and at Beryl Caighn. She has told you that she did. What, then, is there left for you to decide? Whether or not she was attempting to kill her husband, Miss Caighn, or both. I smile. I find it difficult to proceed without bursting into laughter at the childish pimslicity of the answer. And at the puny excuse, well after the fact, that— *(His voice drips with sarcasm)* she only meant to frighten them. Simplicity! This being the case, why not blank cartridges? Why not a cap pistol? Why any pistol at all? Why not simply appearing? That would have been frightening enough. Wouldn't it? As a citizen—a law-abiding citizen—I resent any neighbor who dares to take the law into her own hands—to create an individual interpretation for herself alone. Now as to the character of this Doris Attinger. I'm afraid we know little about it—or about Doris Attinger. We have not seen Doris Attinger here. What we have seen has been a performance complete with costume and make-up. Carefully coached by her artful counsel, she has presented a gentle facade. A sweet face, crowned by a tenderly trimmed little bonnet. I found it difficult to be taken in, ladies and gentlemen, since *I* am the one who paid for the bonnet! *(He draws a slip from his pocket and shows it to the jury)* And here is my receipt to prove it! *(He hands it to* AMANDA) Any objection to my showing it to the Court and to the Jury?

AMANDA *looks at it.*

AMANDA: None.

She hands it back.

ADAM (*giving it to the* BAILIFF): Have it marked Peoples' Exhibit 12. (*He stalks over to* MRS. ATTINGER) And if you don't mind, Mrs. Attinger—I want my hat back! (*He snatches it from her head righteously*)

MRS. ATTINGER: Hey!

She grabs the top of her head as her hair tumbles down, making her a sudden witch.

AMANDA: Your Honor—

ADAM *crumples the hat into a small ball and stuffs it into his pocket.*

AMANDA: Just a moment—

ADAM: Now, as to the efforts of Counsel—][102]

---

[102] In the film, ADAM says: "Well—uh—as I was saying—or, rather, as I was hoping I would be able to say—uh—the purpose of any summation, it seems to me, in any Lourt of Caw—as in any Court of Law—as Cour—" Amanda smiles at him as he continues, "I beg your pardon, ladies and gentlemen. Let me begin again. What is there for you to decide? One thing. Was she trying to kill her husband and Beryl Caighn or both? I smile. I find it a little difficult to proceed in this case without bursting into laughter at the utter plinsicity of (AMANDA smiles and puts her hand over her mouth) the answer and the puny excuse, well after the fact, that she was merely trying to frighten them. Simplicity! I resent—I resent any neighbor who takes the law into her own hands and places a special interpretation upon it, just for herself. Now, let's—let's take the character of this—uh—Doris Attinger. I'm afraid that's going to be a little difficult (he walks toward DORIS) because we haven't been told much about her here. And we certainly haven't seen Doris Attinger in this courtroom. What we have seen is a performance, complete with make-up and co-costume. Coached by the Counsel for the Defense, she has presented a sweet face—what a sweet face—crowned by a tenderly trimmed bonnet. I find it a little difficult to be taken in, ladies and gentlemen, because I happen to be the fellow who paid for the bonnet, and here's the receipt to prove it. Do you mind if I show that to the Court and to the jury?"

AMANDA replies, "Not at all."

ADAM continues, "I'd like to enter this as People's Exhibit No. 12. And, also, Mrs. Attinger—" The JUDGE is heard off-camera saying, "No objection if—" while ADAM turns and leans toward DORIS and grabs the hat from her head, saying, "I would like to have my hat back!" DORIS screams, AMANDA jumps up and says, "Your Honor!" The JUDGE says, "Mr. District Attorney—" and ADAM goes on, "Now, any further attempt by the Counsel for the Defense to turn this into a circus—" The JUDGE says, "—you will conclude your summation without any further demonstration."

Dissolve to:
Insert

> *A front page. A headline reads:*
> [ATTINGER VERDICT TODAY][103]

Dissolve to:

Interior, the Hallway[104]**—Medium Shot,** *near a shingle which reads:*
PRESS ROOM. *The man enters the* SHOT, *opens the Press Room door, and shouts in.*

THE MAN *(a former corporal)*: Okay! Let's go!!

> *He returns quickly. A few newspaper men follow him. They are putting on jackets, settling poker debts, scurrying along. Photographers are readying their cameras. They have a time making their way through the considerable crowd which blocks the courtroom doorway.*

Interior, the Courtroom—Full Shot

[*The* JUDGE *is seated.*][105] *The room continues to fill. The* JUDGE *and the* CLERK *consult one another. The* JURY *is seated. There is a hush. The* CLERK *rises. Everyone looks weary.*

THE CLERK: Mr. Foreman please rise. Have you agreed upon a verdict?

Close Shot—Adam, *nervous.*

THE FOREMAN *(offscreen)*: We have.

---

[103] In the film:

> NEW YORK RECORD
> ATTINGER
> VERDICT
> TODAY
> "Love Triangle" Defendant to Learn Fate

[104] In the film, a sign at the left reads:

> CRIMINAL
> COURT
> No Admittance
> Judge Charging Jury

[105] In the film, the CLERK says, "Please rise." Everyone rises as the JUDGE enters and sits on the bench. The CLERK says, "Please be seated."

Close Shot—Amanda, *pale.*

THE CLERK *(offscreen)*: Jurors please rise— Defendant rise— Jurors look upon the defendant— Defendant look upon the jurors. *(Addressing* FOREMAN*)* How say you? Do you find the defendant guilty or not guilty?

Full Shot—the Room

A pause.

THE FOREMAN: We find the defendant *not* guilty.

A wave of excitement sweeps the room. The formalities continue behind the following.

Close Shot—Amanda

Her victory has a sudden bitter taste.

Close Shot, THE JUDGE, *obviously surprised.*

Medium Shot

ADAM *and staff. Down.* ADAM *is shaking his head with a "beats all" expression.*

Close Shot—Amanda

She looks over at ADAM.

Close Shot—Adam, *packing his briefcase. He looks up at her. His face shows no sign of familiarity.*

Medium Shot—Amanda and Adam

They look at one another. Now MRS. ATTINGER *comes to* AMANDA *and kisses her hand.* AMANDA's *attention is still on* ADAM, *who moves away.*

[Close Shot—Attinger

He gets up and crosses to his wife, the CAMERA FOLLOWING *and* SWELLING IN TO:]

Full Shot

During the above:

THE CLERK *(offscreen)*: Hearken to your verdict as it stands recorded. You say that you find the defendant Not Guilty of the offense as charged in the indictment. And so say you all?

THE FOREMAN *(offscreen)*: Yes, sir.

Medium Shot—the Bench

THE JUDGE *(offscreen)*: Ladies and Gentlemen of the Jury, thank you for your efforts. The Jury is excused, the court is adjourned. *He rises.*[106] *The room rises. He leaves. His exit is the cue for the great noise and excitement. The photographers take charge and shove everyone about for proper pictures.*

Medium Shot

[*Posing for the press,* MR. ATTINGER, MRS. ATTINGER, *and the three kids.*

A PHOTOGRAPHER: Grab her! Grab her!

ANOTHER: Give her a kiss.

ATTINGER *pecks her.*

ANOTHER: A big kiss, you clown.

ATTINGER *gives his wife a big kiss as the photographers work and his children scowl in fear.*

Medium Close Shot

ADAM *at the table. He is conferring with an assistant.*

Medium Close Shot—Amanda, *putting her things away.*

Medium Close Shot

*Posing for the photographers—*MRS. ATTINGER, MR. ATTINGER, *and—*MISS BERYL CAIGHN.

A PHOTOGRAPHER: Smile, smile!

ANOTHER: Laugh!

ANOTHER: More!

---

[106] THE CLERK is heard saying, "Please rise."

96

ANOTHER: Arms around both—around both.

ATTINGER *complies with a foolish grin.*]¹⁰⁷

Medium Shot

> At AMANDA's *table.* AMANDA *looks at* ADAM *hopefully. She smiles. He does not respond. He looks off.*

[**Medium Shot**

> *The trio, grinning. Behind them certain members of the jury are hopping high to make sure they get into the picture.*]

Medium Shot—Adam, *on his way out, the* CAMERA PANNING. *He is suddenly in a:*

Two-Shot, *as he passes* AMANDA's *table. He hesitates a moment, then continues. The* CAMERA HOLDS *on* AMANDA, *looking after him. The background action is lively.* ADAM *steps back into the* SHOT. *He is busy buckling his briefcase.*

ADAM: Congratulations.

AMANDA: Thank you.

ADAM: Or should I say, "Congratulations"?

AMANDA: Yes.

---

¹⁰⁷ In the film, a photographer is heard saying, "Come on honey, let's get a picture right here. Thank you." AMANDA says, "All right." AMANDA and DORIS embrace as photographer takes a picture. Photographers and newspapermen gather around DORIS and lead her toward ATTINGER while others lead him toward her. He puts out his hand and shakes hands with her, they smile as photographers take pictures; all ad lib noisily. ATTINGER kisses DORIS on the cheek as cameras snap away; BERYL comes forward and shakes hands with DORIS, and ATTINGER puts his hand on top of both of theirs. When DORIS sees this she cries out, "Warren!" A woman brings the three Attinger children forward through the crowd. When DORIS sees them she breaks away; a photographer tries to hold her, saying, "Hey, now, wait a minute. One more picture." DORIS cries, "My babies! My babies! My babies!" DORIS embraces the children, then the photographers and reporters pose them for a picture, ad libbing: "Come on. Let's get some pictures of the kids. Come on, son. That's it. Bring the father in." ATTINGER embraces children, then poses with them and DORIS. Ad libbing is heard: "Hold it. Bring Beryl in. Bring Beryl in." BERYL stands behind the family group. Ad libbing is heard: "Put your arms around him. Right around him." (*See film still 23.*)

97

ADAM: Well.

He starts off.

AMANDA: I wish it could have been a tie. [I really do.]

Two photographers, one male, one female (from way up-town) and an officious REPORTER come into the SHOT and take charge.

[THE REPORTER: Stand together there, willya? *(They obey automatically)* Mrs. Bonner, you consider this a significant verdict?

She looks at ADAM, can't speak.

ADAM: Yes, she does.

The photographers are at work.

THE REPORTER *(reading from notes)*: —a small but important step forward in woman's march toward moral equality and justice.

AMANDA: What?

THE REPORTER: Out of the front part of your summation—okay to quote you now?

AMANDA: I suppose so. Yes.

THE REPORTER: Right.

THE MAN PHOTOGRAPHER: Shake hands once.

THE REPORTER: Yeah, do that.

They do, with some awkwardness, since she is as embarrassed by her victory as he is by his defeat. The photographers pop and pop. Now the lady one takes up a Leica on a strap around her neck.

THE LADY PHOTOGRAPHER: Can you look pleasant?

ADAM *(looking out at her)*: Huh?

THE LADY PHOTOGRAPHER: At her! Pleasant.

THE MAN PHOTOGRAPHER *(impatient)*: Let's go, huh?

ADAM *and* AMANDA *look at each other.*

THE LADY PHOTOGRAPHER: Pleasanter! Pleasanter!

They try hard, but with indifferent success. The pictures are made.

THE MAN PHOTOGRAPHER: Thanks loads, kids. *(He goes)*

THE LADY PHOTOGRAPHER: One more.

ADAM *(moving her away)*: Oh, no.

THE LADY PHOTOGRAPHER: Just one more. (ADAM *stands still)*

Arm around her. Come on. Arm around.

ADAM: I don't think—

AMANDA *(turning away)*: That's enough, now, if you don't mind—

THE LADY PHOTOGRAPHER: —What I call *some* cooperation! *(She is off in a huff)*

ADAM: Sorry about the—*(He indicates the camera folk)*

AMANDA: Oh, sure.

ADAM: Well.

AMANDA: Yes.]¹⁰⁸

¹⁰⁸ REPORTER: Stand together, will ya'? Right there. Is that okay—
PHOTOGRAPHERS *(ad libbing)*: All right, can we have one of you looking at her, please? Move a little closer, Mr. Bonner. Smile. Hold it! Right over here." *(See film still 24.)*
REPORTER *(over and above ad libs)*: Mrs. Bonner, do you consider this a significant verdict?
ADAM: Yes, she does.
FEMALE PHOTOGRAPHER: All right. Can you look pleasant at her? Just as though—
REPORTER *(over ad libs)*: Laugh it up, will you, for the cameraman? ". . . A small but important step in woman's march toward equality and justice—"
PHOTOGRAPHER *(ad libbing)*: Smile! You're supposed to be happy—
AMANDA: What?
REPORTER: From the front part of your summation. Okay to quote you now?
AMANDA: Oh, yeah, yeah. I suppose so—
PHOTOGRAPHERS *(ad lib)*: All right, shaking, shaking hands— How about shaking hands? Come on, be friendly. Shake hands. Shake hands. Hold it.
REPORTER *(ad libs)*: That's a good idea. Shake hands. Hold it. All is forgiven.
PHOTOGRAPHERS *(ad lib)*: Swell! Fine. All right, then—just one more. Arm-in-arm.
REPORTER *(ad libs)*: Ah, please. Now, one of you with your hand— Now, one of you two.
ADAM *(ad libs)*: That's enough—
AMANDA *(ad libs)*: That's enough. You'll never get enough—
ADAMS That's enough!
FEMALE PHOTOGRAPHER *(ad libs)*: That's what I call some cooperation.
ADAM: I'm sorry about—
AMANDA: Well—
THE STENOGRAPHER *(comes forward)*: Excuse me, please. Great job, Mrs. Bonner.
AMANDA: Thank you.
ADAM: Well.
AMANDA: Yeah.
A JUROR *(speaking to ADAM over and above ad libs)*: —after all, the evidence—
AMANDA: Adam!
People in the crowd ad lib, "If your husband loves you at all—"

He starts off. AMANDA *takes an instinctive step toward him. He stops, looks at her.*

AMANDA *(quickly)*: You remember we've got to get with Julie over that quarterly tax return? *(ADAM nods)* Tomorrow all right? *(Another nod)* Want me to set it up?

ADAM *(wearing the pants)*: I'll do it.

AMANDA: Thanks.

ADAM: Nothing.

AMANDA: See you.

ADAM: I suppose so.

They split and walk off. The CAMERA RIDES *in better to frame all the photographers still at work. They are trying to make the hapless trio act out a pantomime of* BERYL *giving* ATTIN-GER *back to his wife. Chaos.*

Dissolve:

[Exterior, Bonner Apartment House—Full Shot—Night
Number fifteen, brightly lighted within.][109]

Dissolve to:

Interior, Kip's Apartment—Full Shot
The room. AMANDA *stands by the fireplace, riffling through a legal document. A supper tray is arranged on the tea table.*
KIP *is sitting down, stretched out, relaxed—drink in hand.*

AMANDA *(a faraway tone)*: —a question of the value you place on the residuals of the piece. You see, the principle of retaining copyright—

She stops and studies a paragraph.

KIP: I made a mistake tonight.

AMANDA: So?

KIP: Should have invited your mind to supper, too.

AMANDA *(looking up)*: What?

KIP: Your absent mind.

---

[109] In the film, a title card reads:
THAT EVENING

100

AMANDA: I'm sorry, Kip. *(She hands him the paper)* Sure this is in order, though.

[KIP: Thanks. Have a sandwich.

She takes one.

AMANDA *(a touch of bitterness)*: He thinks I'm unreasonable. Adam.

(See film still 25.)

KIP: Never mind Adam.

AMANDA *continues in a tone of fierce but controlled self-justification.* KIP *goes to the piano and scores the following scene as though it were a silent movie.*

AMANDA: Just as a friend, Kip, do *you* think I'm unreasonable?

KIP *looks her over and thinks.*

KIP *(finally)*: I think you're reasonable.

AMANDA *(her passion rising)*: Do I strike you as overbearing?][110]

KIP: *Under*bearing.

AMANDA: I may be wrong about much—about plenty—but not this!

KIP: Not what?

AMANDA: A marriage. What it's supposed to be. What makes it work—or perfect.

KIP: You're *so* right.

AMANDA: Balance. Equality. Mutual—everything! There's no room in a marriage for what they used to call "the little woman." She's got to be as big as the man is.

KIP: What if he's a little man?

[AMANDA *(unhearing)*: Sharing! That's what it takes to keep a

---

110 Instead, in the film:
KIP: Thanks. Want a drink?
AMANDA: He thinks I'm unreasonable.
KIP: Who?
AMANDA: Adam.
KIP: Oh, never mind Adam.
AMANDA: Well, just, just as a friend, Kip—
KIP: Yes, you beautiful barrister, you.
AMANDA: As a friend, do—do you think—that I'm unreasonable?
KIP: I think you're—reasonable.
AMANDA: Yes. But, but, do, do I strike you, strike you as overbearing?

marriage from getting sick. Of every dot. All the duties and responsibilities and, and troubles and— Listen, no part of life is the exclusive province of any one sex. Why can't he see that?][111]

KIP: Because he's unreasonable.

AMANDA: Well—

KIP: And overbearing.

AMANDA: Sore as he was, that was wrong. To call me a competitor.

KIP: What's that?

AMANDA: A competitor?

KIP: Oh.

AMANDA: What a way to put it.

KIP: He's just miffed because he lost.

AMANDA: Ah, don't be idiotic! *(A sudden thought)* Be something, won't it? Win the case and lose my husband. [*(She puts her sandwich down. Can't eat more)*] Maybe it's a test. If we weather this we'll be better together. And if we don't— *(The catch in her throat stops the speech)*

KIP: Lawyers should never marry other lawyers. This is called inbreeding, from which comes idiot children and more lawyers.

AMANDA: I wish he'd call up. You're sure we can hear my phone in here?

She goes to the open window, opens it wider, and looks across the court.

KIP: Lawyers should marry piano players or song writers or both. How would you like to give me a kiss?

AMANDA: What time is it?

[*She picks up her sandwich and resumes eating.*]

KIP: You wouldn't like to, huh?

AMANDA: Why don't I call him up?

---

[111] Instead, in the film:

AMANDA: Sharing. That's what it takes to make a marriage, keep a marriage from getting sick of all the duties and respons— Now, you're sure that we can hear my phone in here?

KIP: I'm sure.

AMANDA: All those duties and responsibilities and, and troubles. Listen. No part of marriage is the exclusive province of any one sex. Well, now, why can't he see that?

KIP: How would you like me to give *you* a little kiss?

AMANDA: I would—*(KIP sits up)* but I don't know where to call him. That's why.

KIP *relaxes.* [AMANDA *takes a big bite out of her sandwich.*][112]

KIP: Couldn't do it with your mouth full anyway. *(Passionately)* [Amanda—Amanda.][113]

AMANDA: What?

KIP: You mind if I call you Mrs. Bonner?

AMANDA: Mutual everything. Or nothing.

KIP: Mrs. Bonner, I love you. I love lots of girls and women and ladies and so on—but you're the only one I know why I love. [Them. You.] And you know why?'

AMANDA: What?

KIP: Because you live right across the hall. You are mighty attractive in every single way, Mrs. Bonner—but I would probably love anybody just so long as they lived across the hall. It's so convenient! Is there anything worse than that awful taking girls home and that long trip back alone? Want to *trade* kisses? *That's* equal.

AMANDA *(good and angry)*: You look here now, Kip. I'm fighting my prejudice but it's clear that you're behaving like a—like a—I hate to put it this way, but—like a—*MAN*!!

KIP *(shocked)*: Watch your language.

AMANDA *jumps to the window.*

AMANDA: Was that my phone?

[KIP: No.]

Exterior, across the Street from Bonner Apartment House— Medium Long Shot

ADAM *is walking back and forth, looking up. He bumps into a passerby, who doesn't take it well. He stops and looks up.*

---

112 In the film, she eats a cracker.
113 In the film:
AMANDA: But I don't know where he is.
KIP: Amanda! Amanda!

Long Shot—What He Sees

(With a zoom lens we graphically illustrate his mental action.)
His attention rides to a single row of windows, high up. Then
back.

Medium Shot—Adam, *standing on the curb, still looking up. With*
sudden determination, he walks across the street and into the
lobby of the building, the CAMERA FOLLOWING. *We see him*
stride down the hall and enter the elevator. Now the CAMERA
TIPS UPWARD, *slowly.*

Interior, the Hallway

ADAM *steps out of the elevator. He turns to speak to the*
elderly operator.

[ADAM: Lend me your passkey a minute, will you?

THE OPERATOR *(reaching for it)*: Sure thing—

ADAM: What would I do without you, Paddy?][114]

PADDY: You'd remember your key. *(He hands over a large iron*
ring which holds the passkey)

ADAM *(overcasual)*: Don't wait—I'll bring it right down.

PADDY: Sure thing.

The elevator door closes. ADAM *moves down the hall, the*
CAMERA FOLLOWING. *He stops in front of the door to* KIP's
apartment. Now he glances down the hall left, right. From his
briefcase he gets what appears to be a small automatic pistol.
He puts the briefcase under his arm. He draws a deep, deep
breath and makes ready.

Interior, Kip's Apartment—Medium Shot—Kip and Amanda

[KIP: Put it this way. Just go through the motions once—

AMANDA: Oh, stop it, Kip.

KIP: [I'm not asking you to feel anything—] just pretend[, that's
all]. Like they do on the stage, say. Like Lunt and Fontanne.

---

[114] In the film, instead:
ADAM: Oh, uh—could I use your passkey?
OPERATOR *(offscreen)*: Sure thing.
ADAM: What would I ever do without you, Louie?

[Come on.] You be Lunt and I'll be Fontanne—no, other way—
[that's it.]¹¹⁵

He puts his arms about her and begins to twist his head into
position for a kiss as he speaks the above. AMANDA *is avoiding*
consummation with a certain amount of skill but experts would
place their money on KIP. *Now suddenly the door in the back-*
ground of the SHOT *is flung open and* ADAM *bounds into the*
room with a snarl. KIP *and* AMANDA *freeze.* ADAM *is not sure*
what he's supposed to do next.

ADAM *(a whisper)*: All right. Break it up.

KIP *backs away.*

AMANDA *(a tone for lunatics)*: Adam. Adam. Listen to me, Adam.

ADAM: Don't handle me, lady. I'm not nutty. No more than the
average, anyway. You said it today. Anyone is capable if provoked, you said. You bet. Including *me.* Yes. *(*KIP *moves)* Don't
move, man. Stand still as can be.

AMANDA: Adam. Adam.

ADAM: You said that before.

AMANDA: Adam, you're sick. Please. What do you think you're
doing?

ADAM: Teaching a lesson. Him now. Yours comes later. *(*AMANDA
steps in front of KIP *suddenly)* Get away, Amanda.

AMANDA: Adam, stop.

ADAM *moves around.* AMANDA *is shielding* KIP.

ADAM: Get away, Amanda.

KIP *(whispering over her shoulder into her ear)*: Don't you do it,
Amanda.

ADAM *moves in the other direction and raises the pistol.*

AMANDA: Stop it, Adam. Stop it! You've no right! You can't do
what you're doing! *You've no right!*

ADAM: What?

Close Shot—Amanda

AMANDA: No one has a right to—*(She stops, suddenly realizing*
what she has said.)

¹¹⁵ In the film, AMANDA starts to speak: "Okay—"

105

Close Shot—Adam
He smiles.

ADAM: That's all, sister. That's all I wanted to hear [you say]. Music to my tin ear.

Two Shot—Kip and Amanda
They look at each other.

Medium Shot—Adam
He raises the pistol to his lips and puts the muzzle into his mouth.

Two Shot—Kip and Amanda
They are horrified. AMANDA's *eyes double in size.*
[AMANDA: Adam!!]
KIP *screams and averts his head.*

Close Shot—Adam
He bites the muzzle off of the gun and begins to chew it, contentedly, with a gourmet's appraising smile.

Medium Shot—All Three
KIP *and* AMANDA *see without comprehending.* ADAM *takes another bite out of the pistol.*

ADAM *(his mouth full)*: Licorice. If I'm a sucker for anything, it's for licorice.

He finishes the whole pistol and licks his fingers.

AMANDA *(in a white fury)*: I'll never forget this. Never.

ADAM *(hotly)*: Me neither. I'll never forget that no matter what you think you think—you really think the same as I do. That I've no right. That *no one* has a right—to break the law. That your client had no right. That I'm right. That you're wrong.[116]

He starts out; AMANDA *is after him, searching her vocabulary for words to express her feelings. There are no such words.*

[116] In the film, while ADAM is speaking, AMANDA is heard saying, "Despicable —vile—dirty—low—worthless—corrupt."

106

AMANDA: Mean—rotten—dirty—contemptible—little—petty—
gruesome—contemptible—

ADAM *(moving)*: You've said that.

AMANDA: What?

ADAM *(at the door)*: You can finish your wrasslin' match now.

Interior, the Hallway, *as* ADAM *opens door and steps out.*
AMANDA *is running around in front of him.*

AMANDA: You think you can just hit and run—well that's just
where you're wrong—a thing or two to say, too. Or three.

She pushes him into the apartment.

ADAM *(a warning tone)*: Now don't *try* me, Pinkie.

AMANDA *(outraged)*: Don't [you] Pinkie me!

KIP *(stepping to Adam)*: What's biting you, Adam?

ADAM *(nose to nose)*: [What's—*you* are!

AMANDA *starts into the apartment. The* CAMERA FOLLOWS
but as it reaches the threshold the door is slammed (by
AMANDA*) in the* CAMERA'S FACE. *The* CAMERA JUMPS BACK *to
a discreet distance in the hallway. The doors to* KIP'S *apartment, to the Bonner apartment, and to the elevator are all
visible. Now from within* KIP'S *apartment we hear the following:*

KIP *(offscreen)*: I could have you locked up. Yes. Right now.
Tonight, if I felt like it.

ADAM *(simultaneously, offscreen)*: What? What? Listen you. Yes,
and you, too. Don't think you're going to just yell your way out of
this thing because you can't.

AMANDA *(also chiming in, offscreen)*: How dare you! How double
dare you—supposed to be a grown man—nothing but a young—
nothing but a hoodlum.

*There's a crash and a scream, then all three voices dissonantly
blended for a moment. Another crash. The door opens and*
ADAM *comes flying out as though thrown. He is disheveled and
miserable and he hits the opposite wall with some force.*
AMANDA *has followed him out into the hallway.*

AMANDA: Manners of a great big educated ape!

107

The door to KIP's *apartment slams.* ADAM *starts for it, thinks again, goes back to his own door.*

AMANDA *(continuing)*: You think you've humiliated me—tried to —well, that's just where you're wrong, my boy.

ADAM *takes out his keys and bends low to unlock his door.*

AMANDA *(continuing)*: You haven't humiliated anyone with the possible exception of yourself. You've just managed to reveal yourself for what you are. Just couldn't bear to be bested by a woman—isn't that it?

KIP *comes out of his apartment holding a handkerchief to his bloody nose. He sees his opportunity and takes it. A swift kick from him to* ADAM *just as* ADAM *turns the lock (see film still 26)—and* ADAM *falls into his apartment.* AMANDA *follows him in.*

AMANDA *(offscreen)*: The one thing I never thought—

KIP *has turned and started off. Now* ADAM *comes slithering out on the floor and grabs both of* KIP's *ankles.* KIP *falls on his face. (See film still 27.) He and* ADAM *are scrambling to their feet as* AMANDA *comes out into the hall.*

AMANDA: You just stop it now. You're not settling anything behaving like—

ADAM, *with admirable precision, pushes her into their apartment and pushes* KIP *into his own. There's a great crash of a cabinet falling.* ADAM *follows* KIP *in and slams the door on the placating* AMANDA. ADAM *comes out quickly.* AMANDA *grabs him by the lapels.*

AMANDA: All right, now. That's enough.

ADAM: Let go, now.

AMANDA *(near tears)*: I just wouldn't have believed—of all people —you of all—just to degrade me. All you want to be is top dog. I see it now.

ADAM: That's enough yelling out here now for the benefit of all the—

AMANDA: Don't you use that tone to me.

ADAM: If you want to talk this thing out, get into the apartment and we'll talk it out.

AMANDA: Get into the—? You must be joking. I'd be afraid to stay in the same room with a mad bull— I never want to be in the same room with you again as long as I—

ADAM: Suits me fine!

AMANDA: What?!

ADAM: Just once more—you'll just have to be in a room with me once more—to settle up—

AMANDA: All right!

ADAM: Tomorrow—and don't forget!

AMANDA: I won't! And don't you change your mind or try to change mine—

ADAM: Don't worry, lady—I know the end when I see it—

AMANDA: Good for you!

> KIP comes limping into the hallway. There are bits of Spode china all over him. He swings ADAM around and suddenly all three are talking at once.

KIP: I just hope you can afford what you owe me, you great, clumsy oaf! You think you're the only one around here who knows anything about law. Well, there must be a law against you, and if there isn't, I'll see that you get one.

AMANDA (together with the above and below): And I was just on the verge of calling you up— Yes— Imagine that! I almost made the second biggest mistake of my whole life—showing your true colors—may be the best thing ever happened. Yes.

ADAM (simultaneously): Is that so? Well, I don't believe it. Not a word of it. No. And what makes you think *that* would have worked? You think all you've got to do is blow a whistle and I come running. Well, try it. Blow!][117]

---

[117] During this scene, sounds of fighting are heard offstage in KIP's apartment, along with crashes.

ADAM (offscreen): You're biting me. That's what's biting me.

AMANDA (offscreen): How dare you!

KIP (offscreen): I could have you arrested right now.

AMANDA (offscreen): You just get out of here, you—

The door opens and she pushes ADAM into the hall, and he bangs into his apartment door. AMANDA continues, "Manners of a great big educated ape. You think you've humiliated me. Well, that's where you're wrong, my

They finish in what seems to be a dead heat. There has been
a certain amount of twisting-and-turning, stepping-in-front-of,
and finger-in-the-chest poking throughout the above. All geo-
graphic sense has left the contestants. Thus, as they part in a
spurt of simultaneous righteous victory, ADAM *goes into* KIP's
apartment and slams the door. KIP *goes into* ADAM's *and slams*

boy. You haven't humiliated anyone with the possible exception of
yourself."

During this, ADAM starts back toward KIP's door, but it's slammed shut.
He leans over and picks up his topcoat and briefcase from the floor, but as
he rises his briefcase swings up and hits him in the face, and he says, "Ow!"
AMANDA continues, "You've just revealed yourself for what you are. Just
couldn't bear to be bested by a woman, is that it?"

ADAM: All right, all right, that's enough yelling just to let the people—
AMANDA: All you want to be is top dog. Trying to degrade me—

ADAM unlocks the door of his apartment and tosses his topcoat and
briefcase inside, and says, "If you want to talk to me, go on in and sit
down and we'll talk things over. Go on. Get in there and we—"
AMANDA: In that room? Are you joking? I'd be afraid to be in the same
room with a mad bull.

AMANDA pushes him as they argue.
ADAM: Go on and sit down, will you?
AMANDA: I don't want to ever be in the same room with you again.
ADAM: That's fine. That suits me fine.
AMANDA: What?
ADAM: You will be in the same room with me—don't forget that—to
settle things up.
AMANDA: All right!
ADAM: And that's tomorrow and don't forget it! Don't forget it.
AMANDA: I won't! And don't you change your mind or try to change mine.

KIP comes into the hallway, carrying a broken vase; his clothes are torn
and blood is on his face. He says, "I just hope that you can afford to pay
me for what you owe me—"
ADAM: I know when things have come to an end, madam.
KIP:—you great, clumsy oaf, you.
ADAM: Oh, go on now—
AMANDA: And to think that I was on the verge of calling you up!
KIP: You think you know something about law!
ADAM: Call me up!
AMANDA: Imagine that!
KIP: Well, let me tell you, I know something about law, too.
AMANDA: Imagine that. I almost made the second biggest mistake of my
whole life! Showing your true colors!
ADAM: Call me up on the phone! Did you think I'd come running?
KIP: Let me tell you, I know something about law—
AMANDA: May be the best thing that ever happened!
KIP: —and there's gonna be a law against you!

110

the door. AMANDA *stalks to the elevator and rings. The men, meanwhile, realize their mistake, reappear suddenly, start for their proper doors. As they pass one another in mid-hallway, each draws his elbow high in threat. They go through their proper doors, which slam as one.* AMANDA *enters the elevator. The hallway is suddenly still. In the background a door opens. A fat man in a smoking jacket, carrying an unfolded newspaper, steps into the hall, looks up and down, then turns, speaks to his wife inside.*

THE FAT MAN *(angrily)*: [Nobody. Like I told you. Just plain nobody. You must be hearing things. What's the matter with you lately, anyhow? Daffy?][118]

He goes back in, closing the door behind him.

Dissolve to:

[Exterior, Lower Broadway—Full Shot
The financial district, solid and teeming with intention. A man is selling scurrying mechanical ducks in the foreground.][119]

Interior, the Office of Jules Frikke, C.P.A.—Medium Shot
A small room piled high with files and records. In an atmosphere charged with deadlines and desperation, JULES *is cheery*

[118] In the film, instead:
MAN: Nobody. I—I told you—just plain nobody. I don't know what's the matter with you lately. You're always hearing things.
[119] In the film, instead, the camera shoots up to the top of an office building, then pans down to a sign reading:

JULES FRIKKE
CERTIFIED
PUBLIC
ACCOUNTANT

Other signs read:
NOTARY PUBLIC

YOUTH CHINA PRINTING CO.

REAL ESTATE
BONDS

INSURANCE
FIRE—AUTO—LIFE—ETC.

111

and gay. A rotund, bubbling little man, he takes delight in his mathematical prowess and the confused looks on the faces of his clients. ADAM *sits in one of the two visitors' chairs in front of* JULES's *desk.* AMANDA *is in the other chair. Their relationship is strained and formal. They avoid looking at each other.*

JULIE: Now. Here's a check—$337.41 issued to Martin L. Baumer. What's that? It's on the joint account.

ADAM: A furrier.

AMANDA *(almost simultaneously)*: Repairing a coat.

ADAM: Put it down to me, please.

AMANDA: Wait—

ADAM: That coat was a present.

AMANDA: I know—

ADAM: I bought it and it's up to me to keep it in shape.

AMANDA: Not at all.

ADAM: I want to.

AMANDA: I can't help that.

JULIE: Listen, if we're going to debate every one of these it'll take till the next quarter.

ADAM: Okay.

AMANDA: Mine.

JULIE: And not deductible. *(He notes it)* N.D. Now, next is Pollard and Douglas.

AMANDA: Seeds. That's seeds for the house in the country.

JULIE *(a question)*: $478.60?

ADAM: We like a lot of plants.

AMANDA: Liked.

[ADAM: Yes.]

JULIE: N.D. Now—a hundred to Dwight Everly.

ADAM *and* AMANDA *burst into laughter. Suddenly stop.*

ADAM: Nothing. That's a bet we lost. I lost.

JULIE: What kind of bet?

ADAM: What's the difference?

JULIE: N.D. Something you can't tell me?

ADAM: It's nothing. Silly.

JULIE: Uh-huh. Now—Juel Delwyn—$280. You should note all

112

these on your stubs. Save time.

ADAM: That's mine. Not deductible.

JULIE: What is it? Maybe it is.

ADAM: Just some underwear.

JULIE: Underwear?

ADAM: Yes.

JULIE: $280?

ADAM: Not *my* underwear.

JULIE: Very well.

AMANDA *(to* ADAM, *softly)*: Thank you.

JULIE: Now—here. "Bridgeport, Connecticut Citizens Bank—$8740.30." That's what? [Joint account?]

ADAM *(softly)*: That's the final payment on the farm. It's marked on the stub, I'm just *sure,* Julie.

AMANDA: I made it out myself, I know it is.

JULIE: Who said it isn't? Wasn't? The point is, how much of that sum is interest which is deductible and how much actual mortgage payment which is not?

[ADAM *(absently)*: N.D.]

AMANDA: I don't know, do you, Adam?

ADAM: No. I guess we were so excited getting it paid off, finally, we got a little careless.

JULIE: Oh, this was final?

AMANDA: Yes. We own it now. Every scrap.

ADAM: Took us six years.

AMANDA: But we made it!

ADAM *(he can hardly talk)*: Free and clear.

AMANDA: Yes.

A long pause.

Close-up—Adam

Tears are welling up in his eyes.

Close-up—Amanda

She looks at him, turns away. Then looks back.

Close-up—Adam

He looks down, but we see an outsize tear streaming down his rugged cheek.

Close-up—Amanda, *in pain.*[120]

Medium Shot—the Room

AMANDA *(hoarsely)*: Listen, Pinky.

ADAM *(a croak)*: What?

AMANDA: If we started out right now—we could get there in time to have dinner.

ADAM *(a sickly grin)*: And see the dogs?

AMANDA: Of course, there's nothing much in the freeze.

ADAM: You don't want to.

JULIE: We'll be another two hours on this, at least.

AMANDA *(to* ADAM*)*: Yes, I do.

ADAM: But you don't *really* want to.

JULIE: There's a lot more items.

[AMANDA *(to* ADAM*)*: Come on.][121]

ADAM: Where?

[AMANDA: Home.][122]

JULIE: Wait a moment.

> ADAM, *a broken man, is trying hard to pull himself together. His face is in his right hand. He looks up, tries to speak, cannot, goes back to his pose.* AMANDA *goes to him, helps him to his feet, and begins to lead him out gently.*

---

[120] In the film, while this is happening JULES is saying, "You know, there's a new ruling on that. This process could be considered as paying the interest in advance." ADAM rises and goes to the back of the room, and AMANDA follows him. JULES continues, "The taxpayer, however, can deduct this type of interest payment only at the time the mortgage is fully paid. Taxpayers who use the accrual method of accounting can, of course, take the deduction as the interest payments accrued during the life of the mortgage, but I don't know whether that would actually—"

[121] In the film AMANDA, putting his hat on his head, says, "Here. Come on. Come on.

[122] In the film:

AMANDA: Come on. Home. Back to the farm.

JULIE *(continuing)*: You've got to—

AMANDA *(impatiently)*: Oh—sign our name!—give 'em *all* the money—sign anything!

JULIE: This could cost you.

AMANDA *gets* ADAM *through the door and turns back to* JULIE.

AMANDA: What do I care? The more taxes we pay the better we like it, see?

She is gone, leaving a bewildered expert. He has now heard everything.[123]

Dissolve to:

Exterior, the Bonner Country Place—Sandy Hook, Connecticut— Full Shot—A White Cottage, *on a hilltop. It is moonlit now, iridescent. One window only is lighted.*

Dissolve to:

Interior Bedroom—Bonner Country Place—Medium Shot

It is a small room, and old. The ceiling is beamed and irregular. The bed is a huge four-poster with a small sofa at its foot. AMANDA *is building a fire in the fireplace. She is dressed as before, including hat.*

ADAM: Say—

He comes in, surprisingly attired in trousers and pajama tops.

AMANDA: Speaking to me?

ADAM: You were pretty good.

AMANDA: When?

ADAM: All through. Especially on summation. You had me, almost.

AMANDA: Almost.

ADAM *(innocently)*: What?

AMANDA: You weren't so bad yourself, kid.

ADAM: I guess not. *(He goes back in)* Say, we've got a big thing to talk over tomorrow.

AMANDA: What?

---

[123] In the film, there is a dissolve to a title card reading:
AND THAT NIGHT

She lights the fire, gets out the busted bonnet, and works at fixing it.

ADAM: Well—they may want me to run for Supreme Court Justice.[124] The Republicans do. It's a sure seat, practically.

AMANDA: Pinky!

ADAM: That's me, okay. Supreme Court Justice Pinky.

AMANDA: I'm real proud of you.

ADAM *(touched)*: That's what I'd rather hear than anything. Thank you. *(He goes off and instantly we hear him singing offscreen)* "Hello, Amanda,

Here's a hearty welcome to you.

Hello, Amanda,

The battle was fun

But it's done

It's through,

And from now on,

Fair Amanda,

When you're gazing at the stars above

We'll revive that wonderful night

On the veranda,

Sweet Amanda,

And our love."

AMANDA *sits on the small sofa, kicks off her shoes.*

AMANDA: Adam!

He interrupts the song for a beat—just long enough to reply.

ADAM *(offscreen)*: Uh-huh. *(He goes on singing)*

AMANDA: Have the Democrats got a candidate yet?

The song STOPS *abruptly! A moment passes.* AMANDA *removes her hat.* ADAM *appears in the doorway, grim.*

AMANDA *(continuing lightly)*: I was just wondering.

ADAM: You were.

AMANDA: Mmmmm.

ADAM *moves close to her and leans over.*

ADAM: You won't though.

[124] In the film, it's the County Court Judgeship.

116

AMANDA: How do you know?

ADAM: Because I'll cry and then you won't.

AMANDA: What?

ADAM: Like I did in Julie's office today. Got me my way, didn't it? Got me *you* back.

AMANDA: They were real, *those* tears.

ADAM: Sure they were. And I can turn 'em on any time. Us boys can do it, too. See? It's just that we never think to.

Close-up—Amanda
AMANDA: Bunk.

Close-up—Adam
ADAM: Bunk, huh? Watch this. Keep your eye on the eye.

Close-up—Amanda, *watching.*

Close-up—Adam
ADAM: We're having a little fuss, see. Now it looks as though I'm losing. So here they come. Marks. Get set. Go. *(Sure enough, a great tear wells up in* ADAM'*s right eye)* See it?

Close-up—Amanda, *fascinated.*

Close-up—Adam
ADAM: Then I help it along a little. Like this.
He quivers his chin, flexes his cheek muscles.

Close Two-Shot—Adam and Amanda
ADAM: Ah yes, there ain't one of us but hasn't got his little trick. *(He sniffles)*
She smiles, then shrugs.
AMANDA: All right, then. What have you proved? What does *that* show?

ADAM: Shows the score.

AMANDA: Shows what I say is true. No difference between the sexes. None. Men, women. The same.

ADAM: They are, huh?

AMANDA *puts on the bonnet.*

AMANDA *(retreating slightly)*: Well, maybe there *is* a difference. But it's a *little* difference.

ADAM: Yuh. Well, as the French say.

AMANDA: How do they say?

[ADAM: So: *"Grâce à dieu mais il y a un peu au moins."*

AMANDA: Which means—?

ADAM: Which means, "Thank *goodness* for that little difference!"][125] *Her laughter is bottled by his kiss.*

[**Exterior, the Bonner Place—Long Shot—the Cottage,** *one window lighted. The two big trees which guard it silhouetted against the night mackerel sky. A dog is barking. The light goes out. The dog stops. Nothing but moonlight now. And silence. And, all in all, it's the most peaceful sight you ever saw in your life.*]

Fade out:

The End

[125] Instead, in the film:

ADAM: *Vive la différence!*

AMANDA: Which means?

ADAM: Which means: Hurray for that little difference!